# NITROGEN METABOLISM

# IN PLANTS

## George C. Webster

*Associate Professor of Biochemistry*
*The Ohio State University*

ROW, PETERSON AND COMPANY

Evanston, Illinois                    White Plains, New York

Library of Congress "Cataloguing in Source" data
follows the Index.

# Nitrogen Metabolism in Plants

# ROW-PETERSON BIOLOGICAL MONOGRAPHS

*Editor*

*Allan H. Brown, University of Minnesota*

# Preface

The accelerating pace of present-day research in physiology and biochemistry demands that our knowledge of a given area be subjected to constant review. Such review probably serves a threefold need: information on current progress for research workers outside of the special area, education for new investigators (such as graduate students) entering the area, and re-examination of ideas for workers already in the area. The present review concerns the chemical pathways of nitrogen metabolism in plants. In order that the review be adequate (and still remain within the required limitations of space for this monograph series), it has been necessary to limit the discussion strictly to an examination of our current knowledge of the chemical pathways of cellular nitrogen metabolism. This has required the exclusion of much excellent work on soil-nitrogen relationships, the absorption and translocation of nitrogenous substances, the chemistry of both common and exotic nitrogenous compounds, and the influence of various factors (such as virus infection) on nitrogen metabolism. Such information is available in other reviews, however.

This review would not have been possible without the help of many friends. The author wishes to express his appreciation to them, and especially to his colleague, J. E. Varner, for encouragement and aid during the preparation of the manuscript.

*Columbus, Ohio*
*January 20, 1958*

*George Webster*

## *Abbreviations*

| | |
|---|---|
| AMP | adenosine monophosphate |
| ADP | adenosine diphosphate |
| ATP | adenosine triphosphate |
| $As_i$ | arsenate |
| CoA | coenzyme A |
| DNA | deoxyribonucleic acid |
| DPN | diphosphopyridine nucleotide |
| DPNH | reduced diphosphopyridine nucleotide |
| E | enzyme |
| FAD | flavin adenine dinucleotide |
| FMN | flavin mononucleotide |
| GLU | glutamate |
| $GLU\text{-}NH_2$ | glutamine |
| GLU-P | glutamyl phosphate |
| $P_i$ | orthophosphate |
| $P\text{-}P_i$ | pyrophosphate |
| RNA | ribonucleic acid |
| TPN | triphosphopyridine nucleotide |
| TPNH | reduced triphosphopyridine nucleotide |

# Contents

# LIST OF TABLES

# Chapter 1

# Introduction:

# Nitrogen Nutrition

Our knowledge of nitrogen metabolism has developed through several overlapping phases. The first phase encompassed the discovery and characterization of the common nitrogenous constituents in plants. Subsequently, extensive measurements were made of the manner in which these nitrogenous constituents vary under different experimental conditions. In recent years, employment of the tools of the biochemist and biophysicist (especially isotopic techniques) has resulted in the characterization of many of the actual chemical pathways involved in nitrogen metabolism. In some cases the detailed chemical steps in the metabolism of a nitrogenous substance are known, and the enzymes catalyzing each step have been isolated and characterized. In most instances, however, only the general outline of a metabolic sequence is apparent at present, and much interesting research will be necessary before the metabolic pathway is clarified. Although researches up to the present time have shown many of the chemical pathways in nitrogen metabolism to be very complex, the rapid pace of present-day research, together with the continual application of new research techniques, leads one to expect that some knowledge of the exact steps involved in most phases of nitrogen metabolism will be available in the forseeable future.

The known chemical pathways of plant nitrogen metabolism may be divided roughly into four areas: (a) the assimilation of nitrogen, (b) the formation and interconversion of amino acids, (c) the synthesis of amides, peptides, and other simple nitrogenous substances, and (d) the formation and degradation of proteins and nucleic acids. In the following pages, these pathways are summarized.

## NITROGEN NUTRITION

The first questions to be answered in a consideration of nitrogen metabolism are: (a) what nitrogenous substances can be assimilated by plants, and (b) what are the pathways involved in the assimilatory process? The nitrogenous substances assimilated by plants can be divided into four major classes: organic nitrogen, ammonia nitrogen, nitrate nitrogen, and molecular nitrogen. Although a few plants (certain bacteria and algae) can assimilate all four forms of nitrogen, the great majority can utilize only nitrate, ammonia, and various forms of organic nitrogen (Table I). There is, however, a small group of plants capable of using only ammonia or organic nitrogen, and a further small number that can utilize only certain forms of organic nitrogen (Robbins, 1937).

*Metabolism of organic nitrogen compounds.* The credibility of early claims of the utilization of organic nitrogen compounds by plants is lessened by the lack of aseptic techniques employed by the investigators. Obviously, if the organic compound were decomposed by micro-organisms to nitrate or ammonia prior to its assimilation, the results indicate nothing concerning the plant's ability to use the intact organic substance. Under aseptic conditions, in fact, the growth of both excised tomato roots (White, 1937) and

TABLE I

Utilization of Various Forms of Nitrogen by Plants[1]

| Group | Organism | Organic nitrogen | Ammonia nitrogen | Nitrate nitrogen | Molecular nitrogen |
|-------|----------|:----------------:|:----------------:|:----------------:|:------------------:|
| I | Some fungi (*Endomyces, Phycomyces*); some bacteria; and some species of *Euglena* | × | | | |
| II | Some fungi (*Mucor, Rhizopus*); some bacteria | × | × | | |
| III | Most bacteria, fungi, algae and higher plants | × | × | × | |
| IV | Some bacteria and blue-green algae | × | × | × | × |

[1] Adapted from Robbins (1937).

cress roots (Andrus and Quastel, 1947) is inhibited by a number of different amino acids. In the case of orchid embryos (Spoerl, 1948), only arginine promotes growth, while each of eighteen other amino acids is inhibitory. However, Ghosh and Burris (1950), in an extensive study, found that a wide variety of amino acids can be used by clover and by tomato plants. Of these, alanine, arginine, asparagine, glutamate, glycine, histidine, isoleucine, leucine, lysine, and phenylalanine are better nitrogen sources than ammonia for clover. Alanine, asparagine, glutamate, histidine, and phenylalanine are better than either ammonia or nitrate. In tomato plants, a number of amino acids are better nitrogen sources than ammonia, but only glutamate is utilized more readily than nitrate. In tobacco, nitrate and ammonia are superior to all organic nitrogen compounds that have been examined. Ratner, et al. (1956) have found that corn and sunflower plants can grow with glycine, aspartate, glutamate, or arginine as their sole sources of nitrogen, but that none of these substances is as effective as inorganic nitrogen. Lysine and alanine are used only poorly, while phenylalanine and tyrosine inhibit growth. In contrast, Chlorella has been observed to grow faster in the presence of several different amino acids than with either nitrate or ammonia (Ghosh and Burris, 1950; Arnow, et al., 1953). It is evident from this work that some plants can not only utilize amino acids as a nitrogen source, but also that these amino acids are sometimes better nitrogen sources than ammonia or nitrate. Presumably, in most of these cases, the amino acid is absorbed by the cells as such, and is simply fed into the metabolic machinery of the cell. Virtanen and Linkola (1946) have reported that aspartate and glutamate are taken up in intact form and utilized as a nitrogen source by both peas and clover. Ratner, et al. (1956) have found $C^{14}$-tyrosine to be taken up as a unit by corn and sunflower roots. Likewise, when radioactive glutamate is given to bean seedlings, the intact glutamate molecule enters the cell and forms a pool of free glutamate inside the cells (Webster, 1954). Evidently, the glutamate is absorbed by the cells faster than it is metabolized, as the glutamate eventually is found in glutamine, glutathione, and protein. When radioactive aspartate is given to lupine seedlings, a similar accumulation of free aspartate in the cells takes place, although the greater portion of the aspartate is converted to asparagine (Webster and Varner, 1955a). The subsequent utilization of these pools of free glutamate and aspartate in various synthetic and degradative processes (Webster, 1954; Webster and Varner, 1955a) leaves little doubt that at least some plants can incorporate amino acids directly into their metabolic pathways.

In the case of plant tissue cultures, a somewhat different situation exists. Individual amino acids generally have no promoting effect on growth. In fact, as mentioned earlier, they often cause growth inhibition (White, 1937; Andrus and Quastel, 1947; Riker and Gutsche, 1948). Mixtures of amino acids, however, have been shown to enhance appreciably the growth of cultures of several different tissues (Paris and Duhamet, 1953; Straus and LaRue, 1954; Netien and Beauchesne, 1954). The effectiveness of mixtures of amino acids may be of considerable significance. The ability of individual amino acids to be better nitrogen sources than inorganic nitrogen is dependent upon two factors: (a) a faster rate of absorption than inorganic nitrogen sources, and (b) the availability of amino groups for transfer to other keto acids faster than they can be transferred following assimilation of inorganic nitrogen. It is not surprising, therefore, that individual amino acids often fail to provide nitrogen as effectively as ammonia or nitrate. In the case of amino acid mixtures, however, the necessity for transfer of amino groups no longer exists, provided all amino acids are taken up readily by the cells, and thus such mixtures could well serve as efficient sources of nitrogen. Unfortunately, extensive studies on the relative efficiency of amino acid mixtures in comparison with single amino acids have not been performed. Likewise, little is known concerning the relative rates of cellular absorption of amino acids and inorganic forms of nitrogen.

In addition to studies with amino acids, many investigations on the utilization of organic nitrogen compounds have dealt with urea, which has been demonstrated to serve as a nitrogen source for a large number of plants. Urea is absorbed as an intact molecule by bean plants, and forms a pool of free urea in the cells before it is metabolized (Webster, et al., 1955b). In some higher plants, urea may be hydrolyzed to carbon dioxide and ammonia (Hinsvark, et al., 1953). Studies with $C^{14}$-urea in bean plants have shown that the radioactive carbon is incorporated into many amino acids and into protein in the same general pattern as is obtained with $C^{14}$-carbon dioxide (Webster, et al., 1955b). Likewise, the absorption of $N^{15}$-urea results in an incorporation of $N^{15}$ into amino and amide nitrogen in a fashion comparable with that obtained with ammonia (Boynton, et al., 1953). The possibility must not be overlooked, however, that the carbamyl group of urea is used directly, and there is some indirect evidence (Walker, 1952; Steward and Pollard, 1956) that this is the case. This possibility requires further study.

In this connection, the recent findings of Slocum (1958) on urease activity are of interest. It has been known for some time that phosphate inhibits and arsenate promotes the urease-catalyzed hydrolysis of urea. Slocum allowed urease to act on urea in the presence of phosphate or arsenate labeled with oxygen-18. Under these circumstances, the carbon dioxide liberated from urea contained oxygen-18. The results suggest that urease is capable of catalyzing the reactions:

$$\text{urea} + \text{phosphate} \longrightarrow \text{carbamyl phosphate} + NH_3$$

$$\text{urea} + \text{arsenate} \longrightarrow \text{carbamyl arsenate} + NH_3$$

As carbamyl phosphate is probably more stable than carbamyl arsenate, arsenate might well be expected to enhance urea hydrolysis while phosphate inhibits hydrolysis. These interesting experiments indicate that urease may catalyze some carbamyl transfer reaction which is part of the normal nitrogen metabolism of the plant cell. The hydrolytic activity of urease could result simply from its ability to transfer a carbamyl group, much like the phosphatase activity of glyceraldehyde phosphate dehydrogenase and the glutamyl transfer ability of glutamine synthetase.

Aside from amino acids and urea, most of the other organic nitrogen compounds which have been examined are very poor nitrogen sources for plants. The value of organic nitrogen compounds for normal plant nutrition, therefore, would appear to be a function either of the ease with which they can be decomposed to form ammonia, or of the efficiency with which they can be incorporated into the normal metabolic cycles of the plant cells.

*Metabolism of ammonia.* Our knowledge of the metabolic fate of ammonia in cells has been aided immeasurably by the use of isotopic $N^{15}H_3$. Thus, Vickery, *et al.* (1940) demonstrated that the nitrogen of $N^{15}H_3$ is incorporated by tobacco plants into amides, amino acids, and proteins. Similar findings were reported by Hevesy, *et al.* (1940) with sunflower plants. These experiments were extended by MacVicar and Burris (1948), who showed that glutamic and aspartic acids become highly labeled with $N^{15}$ from $N^{15}H_3$. Their results suggest that glutamate and aspartate are primary products of the assimilation of ammonia by plants. In agreement with these conclusions are the findings of Rautanen (1948) that glutamate, aspartate, their amides, and alanine are the major products of ammonia uptake.

The detailed manner in which all of these products are formed is only partially understood at present. The extremely high labeling of glutamate is almost certainly the result of its direct production by the reductive amination of $\alpha$-ketoglutarate. The enzyme catalyzing this reaction, glutamic dehydrogenase, has been isolated from a number of plant sources (Adler, *et al.*, 1938; Damodaran and Nair, 1938; Bulen, 1956), and the reaction shown to proceed as follows:

$$\alpha\text{-ketoglutarate} + NH_3 + DPNH + H^+ \rightleftharpoons$$
$$\text{glutamate} + DPN^+ + H_2O$$

Glutamic dehydrogenase has been purified about forty-six-fold from corn leaves by Bulen (1956). The enzyme is specific for DPN, unlike the TPN-specific dehydrogenase from yeast and bacteria, or the glutamic dehydrogenase of animals which can use either coenzyme.

The manner in which ammonia is incorporated into aspartate is not so clear. Three possible pathways have been suggested:

$$\text{fumarate} + NH_3 \rightleftharpoons \text{aspartate} \tag{a}$$

$$\text{oxalacetate} + NH_3 + DPNH \text{ (or TPNH)} + H^+ \rightleftharpoons$$
$$\text{aspartate} + DPN^+ + H_2O \tag{b}$$

$$\text{oxalacetate} + \text{glutamate} \rightleftharpoons \text{aspartate} + \alpha\text{-ketoglutarate} \tag{c}$$

Virtanen and Tarnanen (1932) have found the enzyme, aspartase, which catalyzes the direct amination of fumarate, in seedlings and in leaves of green plants. The occurrence of a reductive amination of oxalacetate has not been demonstrated, but the recent finding of Zelitch (1957) of a DPN-dependent deamination of aspartate in plants suggests the presence of an aspartic dehydrogenase that may be similar to glutamic dehydrogenase. The transfer of the amino group of glutamate to oxalacetate by transamination has been clearly demonstrated (Chapter 2). Thus, it is possible that enzymes catalyzing all three activities may be present in plants. The same degree of uncertainty holds true in the case of alanine formation, where either a reductive amination of pyruvate or a transamination of pyruvate with glutamate is possible. Such reactions have been reported to occur in cell-free extracts of either higher plants or yeast (Chapter 2).

The relative importance of these reactions to the cellular assimilation of ammonia cannot be stated with certainty at present. When $N^{15}$-ammonia is taken up by cells, it is usually incorporated most readily into glutamate, followed by its incorporation into aspartate and alanine. This could be due to a vigorous amination of $\alpha$-ketoglutarate concomitant with less active aminations of oxalacetate and pyruvate. Alternatively, the principal pathway of ammonia assimilation could be chiefly or entirely through the formation of glutamate, followed by the transfer of ammonia to other substances by transamination. The surprising number of substances that will undergo transamination with glutamate

(Chapter 2) is in accord with this concept. Unequivocal evidence for either of these possibilities is difficult to obtain. However, Fincham (1950, 1951, 1954) has observed that two strains of *Neurospora crassa*, which grow only very slowly on ammonia, lack glutamic dehydrogenase. They also lack the ability to form other α-amino acids from ammonia to any significant extent, but apparently contain normal transamination activities. Normal growth can be obtained by substituting glutamate or, to a lesser extent, other amino acids, for ammonia. These findings indicate that initial ammonia assimilation in *Neurospora* proceeds almost entirely through the formation of glutamate by glutamic dehydrogenase. It would not be surprising if a similar situation exists in other plants.

Regardless of the relative importance of the pathways involved, all evidence supports the aminative formation of glutamate, and either the aminative or transaminative formation of aspartate and alanine as the chief means by which ammonia is incorporated into the metabolic pathways of plant cells (Figure 1).

*Utilization of nitrate.* Numerous investigations have established that nitrate is reduced by plants to ammonia. For example, Warburg and Negelein (1920) showed that incubation of *Chlorella* suspensions in nitrate resulted in a disap-

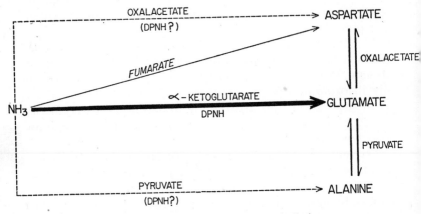

Figure 1. Pathways of ammonia assimilation.

pearance of nitrate and an accumulation of ammonia in the surrounding medium. Similar results were subsequently obtained with higher plants. (Pearsall and Billimoria, 1937; Rautanen, 1948). Both Delwiche (1951) and Mendel and Visser (1951) have demonstrated that the nitrogen of $N^{15}$-nitrate is readily converted to $N^{15}$-ammonia by various plants, and that the distribution of $N^{15}$ in different organic fractions follows the same pattern regardless of whether $N^{15}$-nitrate or $N^{15}$-ammonia is given to the plant. The conversion is strictly a reduction of nitrate to ammonia, however, as Delwiche (1951) showed that $N^{15}$-ammonia is not converted to $N^{15}$-nitrate. The mechanism by which nitrate is reduced to ammonia has remained obscure for a long time. Meyer and Schultze (1894) apparently first suggested the pathway might be:

nitrate → nitrite → hyponitrite → hydroxylamine → ammonia

Until recently, evidence for the occurrence of this pathway, or of any of the suspected intermediates was rather meager, and rested principally on the detection of small quantities of nitrite and hydroxylamine in plants (Lemoigne, *et al.*, 1936, 1937; Michlin, 1938; Virtanen and Ahrimo, 1939).

*Nitrate reductase.* Our knowledge of the actual mechanism by which nitrate is reduced began with the isolation by Evans and Nason (1952, 1953, 1954) of an enzyme from both higher plants and *Neurospora* which catalyzes nitrate reduction by the following reaction:

$$NO_3^- + TPNH + H^+ \rightleftharpoons NO_2^- + TPN^+ + H_2O$$

Although the *Neurospora* enzyme is fairly specific for TPNH, a soybean enzyme can use TPNH or DPNH equally well. The reductase from each source has been purified some sixty- to seventy-fold, and extensive studies have been made on the properties of the isolated enzymes. Reductase activity has been found in extracts of six other plant tissues in addition to soybean and *Neurospora*. A specific DPNH-nitrate reductase has been found in soybean nodules (Evans, 1954). The pyridine nucleotide-nitrate reductase would seem, therefore, to occur generally in plants.

Aside from its probable importance to the cellular conversion of nitrate to ammonia, the nitrate reductase itself has many properties of interest. Analysis has shown the enzyme to be a flavoprotein with flavin adenine dinucleotide as the prosthetic group. The strong inhibitions of reductase activity obtained with cyanide, azide, thiourea, o-phenanthroline, and 8-hydroxyquinoline suggest the involvement of a metal in reductase action. Nicholas, Nason, and McElroy (1954) have identified the metal as molybdenum. The accumulation of nitrate in plants suffering from molybdenum deficiency (Anderson and Spencer, 1950; Hewitt and Jones, 1947; Wilson and Waring, 1948; Mulder, 1948) appears, therefore, to be a direct reflection of decreased nitrate reductase resulting from a deficiency of the essential metal constituent.

The manner in which molybdenum acts in nitrate reduction is becoming clear. It has been suggested (McElroy and Nason, 1954) that molybdenum acts as an electron carrier between reduced FAD and nitrate in the following manner:

$$\text{TPNH} \rightarrow \text{FAD} \rightarrow \text{MO} \rightarrow \text{NO}_3^-$$

Evidence in favor of this sequence has been provided by Nicholas and Nason (1954). They find that the molybdenum-free enzyme has lost its ability to catalyze the reduction of nitrate by TPNH or reduced FAD, but will catalyze the reduction of FAD by TPNH. Addition of molybdate restores the lost abilities. That molybdenum acts as an electron carrier is also indicated by the ability of chemically reduced molybdenum to serve as an electron donor for nitrate reduction in the absence of TPNH or reduced FAD.

In addition to the involvement of FAD and molybdenum in reductase activity, the enzyme also requires the presence of free sulfhydryl groups. Nicholas and Nason (1954) have found that the sulfhydryl groups are chiefly concerned with the reduction of FAD by TPNH. They suggest the sulfhydryl groups either function as electron carriers or are involved in binding TPNH or FAD to the enzyme.

*Nitrite reduction.* In connection with their studies on nitrate reductase, Evans and Nason (1953) showed that plant extracts catalyze a slow disappearance of nitrite in the presence of TPNH. This nitrite disappearance is inhibited some 80% by 0.001 M hydroxylamine. Vanecko and Varner (1955) found that $N^{15}$-nitrite is reduced to amino nitrogen by intact leaves in both light and darkness, the rate of reduction in the light being ten to twenty times that in darkness. Their results indicate that nitrite is reduced to the level of ammonia, and are in accordance with the formulation:

$$2HNO_2 + 2H_2O \rightarrow 2NH_3 + 3O_2$$

where photochemical splitting of water provides the reducing power for the reaction.

A purified nitrite reductase has not yet been prepared, but Nason, Abraham, and Averbach (1954) have prepared an enzyme system from both *Neurospora* and soybean leaves that converts nitrite to ammonia. The system can use either DPNH or TPNH, and apparently is a flavoprotein. For each mole of nitrite reduced, three moles of reduced pyridine nucleotide are oxidized. Medina and Nicholas (1957; Nicholas, 1957) have reported that nitrite reduction requires both iron and copper, and that hyponitrite is the product of the reduction. In agreement with this, Frear (1955) has observed that $N^{15}$-hyponitrite can be reduced by plant preparations to the level of ammonia. Furthermore, Medina and Nicholas (1957) have found an enzyme in *Neurospora crassa* that will reduce hyponitrite to hydroxylamine in the presence of DPNH. The activity of the enzyme requires both iron and copper, and is inhibited by metal chelating agents and by sulfhydryl reagents. It is also inhibited by dinitrophenol.

*Hydroxylamine reductase.* The final step in the reduction sequence suggested by Meyer and Schultze (1894) is the reduction of hydroxylamine to ammonia. An enzyme catalyzing this reaction has been found in both *Neurospora* (Zucker and Nason, 1955) and higher plants (Frear and Burrell, 1955). The reductase from *Neurospora* has been purified partially and its activity studied in some detail. It catalyzes the reaction:

$$NH_2OH + DPNH + H^+ \rightarrow NH_3 + DPN^+ + H_2O$$

Present evidence indicates that hydroxylamine reductase, like nitrate reductase, is a metallo-flavoprotein. Nicholas (1957) has reported that the activity depends upon the presence of manganese.

The above experiments on nitrate, nitrite, hyponitrite, and hydroxylamine reduction all support the thesis that nitrate reduction can proceed via these intermediates to ammonia, and that such a sequence may be an important pathway of nitrate reduction in plants. The possible existence of other pathways must not be ignored, however. In addition to a strictly inorganic pathway, it is possible that nitrogen, probably after the initial reduction of nitrate to some intermediate, is conjugated with an organic molecule, and reduced to the amino group level. For example, Virtanen and Ahrimo (1939) have suggested that the pathway of hydroxylamine reduction may not always proceed through the formation of free ammonia. Instead, the following sequence is postulated:

$$NH_2OH + \alpha\text{-keto acid} \rightarrow \text{oxime} \rightarrow \alpha\text{-amino acid}$$

Definitive evidence for this pathway is not available, however. Studies on nitrate reduction by a series of *Neurospora* mutants (Silver and McElroy, 1954; McElroy and Spencer, 1956) support the view that nitrate reductase is operative in the normal pathway of nitrate reduction, but that free hyponitrite and hydroxylamine may not be on the principal pathway of nitrite reduction. Instead, the *Neurospora* studies are in agreement with the pathway of hydroxylamine reduction presented below, which involves pyridoxal:

$$\text{pyridoxal phosphate} + NH_2OH \rightarrow \text{pyridoxal phosphate oxime}$$

$$\text{pyridoxal phosphate oxime} \rightarrow \text{pyridoxamine phosphate}$$

$$\text{pyridoxamine phosphate} + \alpha\text{-keto acid} \rightarrow$$

$$\text{pyridoxal phosphate} + \text{amino acid}$$

It is possible that any or all of the above pathways are operative in different plants, but their acceptance must await critical experiments, both with mutants and with appropriate isotopic techniques.

*Effect of various factors on the assimilation of nitrate and ammonia.* A huge literature has grown up over the years concerning the effects of various environmental conditions on nitrogen assimilation by plants. Many of the observations concern effects on the availability of various nitrogen sources in the soil. These will not be discussed here as they have been reviewed so thoroughly by Nightingale (1937, 1948). A second class of environmental factors affect nitrogen assimilation by affecting respiration. As is the case with other ions, the accumulation of nitrate and ammonia by roots is dependent upon respiratory energy. Therefore, any factor which influences respiration (oxygen tension, temperature, carbohydrates, respiratory inhibitors, etc.) also influences the metabolism of nitrate and ammonia in an explainable manner.

Nitrate and ammonia, however, differ markedly in their response to certain environmental factors. For example, the pH of the nutrient medium exerts a considerable influence on the relative utilization of nitrate and ammonia. In general, a low pH favors nitrate uptake, while a high pH favors the uptake of ammonia (Arrington and Shive, 1935). The age of the plant also influences nitrogen assimilation. Thus, rice utilizes ammonia, but can utilize nitrate only very poorly when young. However, rice gains the ability to assimilate nitrate when mature (Bonner, 1946). Likewise, both wheat and oat seedlings assimilate ammonia better than nitrate, but attain the ability to assimilate nitrate equally well upon maturation (Theelin and Beaumont, 1934; Sessions and Shive, 1933).

Depending upon the plant, either ammonia or nitrate can be absorbed faster than it is assimilated. For example, 56% of the total nitrogen of *Amaranthus* and 80% of the soluble nitrogen of celery have been reported to be in the form of nitrate. Ammonia often is stored in plants with acid sap in the form of the ammonium salts of organic acids. *Begonia* leaves, in the dark, sometimes accumulate up to 30% of their total nitrogen as such ammonium salts. These situations are undoubtedly atypical, however.

*Utilization of molecular nitrogen.* As pointed out earlier, only a limited number of organisms possess the ability to assimilate molecular nitrogen. These include: (a) species of photosynthetic bacteria, (b) species of *Azotobacter, Clostridium, Rhizobium,* and other genera, (c) at least one species of *Rhodotorula,* and (d) several species of blue-green algae (*Nostocaceae*). The manner in which these organisms transform molecular nitrogen into organic forms is of considerable interest, and has elicited a vast amount of investigation over the years, which has resulted in an equally vast literature. Although the exact chemical steps involved in nitrogen fixation are not known, a number of important observations bearing on the mechanism have appeared.

*Requirements for nitrogen fixation.* The assimilation of molecular nitrogen has exhibited no unique requirements. A survey of the optimal conditions for fixation (Wilson, 1940; Burk and Burris, 1941) suggests that those conditions which result in a vigorous metabolic rate are optimal for nitrogen fixation. A supply of metabolic substrate (carbohydrate or other material), and, in the aerobic organisms, a supply of oxygen, are necessary for fixation. No necessity for specific organic cofactors has as yet been found. Although nitrogen-fixing organisms show rather marked responses to calcium, iron, and molybdenum, it is not clear that any of these metals participate directly in the nitrogen-fixing system. The increased requirement of *Azotobacter* for molybdenum when cells are grown on molecular nitrogen instead of ammonia is of considerable interest, but unequivocal evidence for the direct participation of molybdenum in the nitrogen-fixing system must await the isolation and purification of the system.

*Inhibition of nitrogen fixation.* Inhibitors of nitrogen fixation may be grouped into several classes: (a) inhibitors of cellular metabolism (b) hydrogen (c) various nitrogenous substances, and (d) tungsten. In view of the seeming dependence of nitrogen-fixation on normal metabolism in the cell, it is not surprising that various inhibitors of metabolism also inhibit nitrogen fixation. In the case of carbon monoxide, however, nitrogen fixation by *Azotobacter* is far more sensitive than is respiration or nitrate assimilation (Lind and Wilson, 1942). Carbon monoxide, therefore, seemingly affects some portion of the actual nitrogen-fixing process.

The spectacular inhibition of nitrogen fixation by hydrogen has aroused considerable interest (Wilson and Burris, 1947; Wyss and Wilson, 1941; Burris and Wilson, 1945). The facts are that hydrogen competitively inhibits nitrogen fixation in *Azotobacter* and other aerobic organisms (Wilson, *et al.*, 1938), although it has no effect on nitrogen fixation by the anaerobic organism, *Clostridium Pasteurianum* (Rosenblum and Wilson, 1950). In addition, nitrogen inhibits the photo-production of hydrogen by *Rhodospirillum rubrum* (Kamen and Gest, 1949). These facts, plus some indirect evidence, have led to the hypothesis that hydrogenase (the enzyme which activates molecular hydrogen) is implicated in nitrogen fixation. Objections to this hypothesis have been: (a) hydrogenase occurs in organisms that do not fix nitrogen, (b) hydrogenase activity is seemingly absent from nitrogen-fixing root nodules, and (c) no direct evidence is available implicating hydrogenase in nitrogen fixation. The first objection, of course, is without merit, as organisms devoid of the ability to fix nitrogen may be devoid of some enzyme, other than hydrogenase, necessary for nitrogen fixation. The lack of hydrogenase activity in root nodules has always been a far more serious objection, but Hoch, *et al.* (1957) have now provided evidence for the presence of hydrogenase in root nodules. Direct evidence for the participation of hydrogenase in nitrogen fixation is not available. Two observations of considerable interest have been made, however. First, in both *Azotobacter* and *Rhodospirillum*, the hydrogenase content of cells grown on molecular nitrogen is far greater than in cells grown on combined nitrogen (Lee and Wilson, 1943; Gest, *et al.*, 1956). Secondly, Hamilton, *et al.* (1957) have observed that the absorption spectrum of purified hydrogenase from *Clostridium Pasteurianun* is altered markedly by nitrogen, but is not affected by helium. These observations do not constitute proof of the participation of hydrogenase in nitrogen fixation, however, and much more information is necessary before hydrogenase can be assigned such a role. In this connection, it should be pointed out that the hydrogenase activity usually measured by investigators is not necessarily the activity the enzyme catalyzes *in vivo*. It seems likely that definitive information on the mechanism of action (if any) of hydrogenase in nitrogen fixation must await the isolation of the nitrogen-fixing system.

The nitrogenous compounds that inhibit nitrogen fixation fall into two groups: (a) ammonia and substances readily converted into ammonia, and (b) substances not obviously converted into ammonia. Table II shows the effects of ammonia and related nitrogenous substances on nitrogen fixation. It can be seen that their effectiveness varies with their probable availability as sources of free ammonium ions. The observed inhibitions, therefore, are undoubtedly all inhibitions of nitrogen fixation by ammonia. In other cases, however, nitrogenous substances are not so obviously converted into ammonia in order to act as inhibitors. Thus, hydroxylamine and hydrazine probably inhibit nitrogen fixation by inhibiting respiration. In contrast, nitrous oxide is a specific and competitive inhibitor of nitrogen fixation (Molnar, *et al.*, 1948), and seems to act at the site of utilization of molecular nitrogen. It is assimilated at about 5% of the rate of nitrogen (Mozen and Burris, 1954), and probably acts as a true competitor.

TABLE II

Effects of Ammonia and Other Nitrogenous Substances on Nitrogen Fixation[1]

| Addition to system | Per cent inhibition of nitrogen fixation |
|---|---|
| Ammonia | 100. |
| Nitrate | 80. |
| Nitrite | 86. |
| Asparagine | 26. |
| Aspartate | 9. |
| Glutamate | 3. |

[1] Adapted from Wilson and Burris (1947). Cultures previously kept on a nitrogen-free medium.

The inhibition of nitrogen fixation by tungsten is still a different sort of inhibition, and depends upon the fact that cells have an increased need for molybdenum when growing on molecular nitrogen instead of ammonia (Mulder, 1948; Horner, *et al.*, 1942; Jensen, 1947). As tungsten is in the same chemical group as molybdenum, one might expect tungsten either to replace molybdenum or to act as a competitive inhibitor of molybdenum function. No critical evidence is available that tungsten can replace molybdenum in normal cellular activity, but tungsten has long been known as a competitive inhibitor of molybdenum function, and acts as a competitor during nitrogen fixation (Keeler and Varner, 1957a; Takahashi, *et al.*, 1957). This is apparently due to tungsten being incorporated into cellular molybdoprotein in place of molybdenum (Keeler and Varner, 1957b).

*Mechanism of nitrogen fixation.* Despite an impressive amount of research, the mechanism by which nitrogen-fixing organisms use molecular nitrogen is still not known. Although hydroxylamine has been proposed as an intermediate, evidence for its participation is not convincing. On the other hand, experiments with $N_2^{15}$ have established that ammonia, either free or combined in glutamate or aspartate, is the principal end-product of fixation. This has been demonstrated both by kinetic studies (Burris and Wilson, 1946a, b) in which the pattern of amino acid and amide labeling in an organism is the same whether $N^{15}H_3$ or $N_2^{15}$ is employed (Table III), and by the isolation of the $N^{15}H_3$ excreted by *Clostridium* in an atmosphere of $N_2^{15}$ (Zelitch, *et al.*, 1951).

A number of pathways between $N_2$ and $NH_3$ may be postulated. As is seen by reference to Figure 2, these possibilities include an initial oxidation, hydration, or reduction of molecular nitrogen. Many possibilities exist in addition to those presented here, including an early binding of the "activated" nitrogen to an organic molecule (such as α-ketoglutarate or a close relative) and reduction of the bound nitrogen. Unfortunately, it has not been possible as yet to obtain unequivocal evidence for any intermediate between molecular nitrogen and ammonia. Experiments with various suspected

TABLE III

Incorporation of $N^{15}$ into Nitrogenous Fractions
of Microorganisms[1]

| Fraction | *Azotobacter vinelandii* | | | *Nostoc Muscorum* | |
|---|---|---|---|---|---|
| | $N^{15}H_4^+$ | $N_2^{15}$ | $N_2^{15}$ | $N^{15}H_4^+$ | $N_2^{15}$ |
| | 15 min. | 15 min. | 90 min. | 120 min. | 120 min. |
| | Atom per cent excess $N^{15}$ | | | | |
| Total hydrolysate | 1.049 | 0.165 | 0.275 | 1.055 | 0.352 |
| Ammonia | 0.98 | 0.19 | 0.33 | 1.45 | 0.46 |
| Glutamate | 2.55 | 0.25 | 0.50 | 2.36 | 0.66 |
| Aspartate | 0.83 | 0.18 | 0.38 | 0.78 | 0.51 |
| Alanine | — | — | — | 0.44 | 0.27 |
| Leucine | 0.60 | — | — | 0.45 | 0.48 |
| Tyrosine | 0.76 | — | — | 0.25 | 0.08 |
| Histidine | 0.63 | — | 0.21 | 0.31 | 0.26 |
| Arginine | 0.67 | — | 0.19 | — | 0.32 |

[1] Adapted from Wilson (1952).

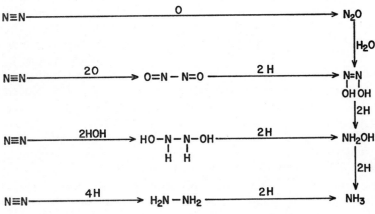

Figure 2. Possible pathways of nitrogen fixation.

intermediates (hydroxylamine, nitrous oxide, nitramide, etc.)
have been disappointing.

Bach and Burris (1957) have found, however, that $N^{15}$-hydrazine is converted to $N^{15}$-ammonia. Between 60 and 90%

of the assimilated hydrazine can be recovered as dihydro-pyridazinone-5-carboxylic acid (Figure 3) and two related substances formed during the reaction of hydrazine and α-ketoglutarate (Otani and Meister, 1957). Dihydropyrida-zinone-5-carboxylic acid occurs in both *Azotobacter* cells and soybean nodules. In soybean nodules given $N_2^{15}$, dihydro-pyridazinone-5-carboxylic acid has an $N^{15}$ concentration as high or higher than is found in glutamate or ammonia (hitherto the substances with the highest $N^{15}$ content). Furthermore, in *Azotobacter*, dihydropyridazinone-5-carboxylic acid has a much higher $N^{15}$ concentration when the cells are incubated with $N_2^{15}$ than when they are incubated with $N^{15}$-ammonia. All of these facts are consistent with dihydro-pyridazinone-5-carboxylic acid or a related compound, being a possible intermediate in nitrogen fixation, and suggest that nitrogen fixation may proceed by a reductive pathway, in-volving hydrazine and dihydropyridazinone-5-carboxylic acid.

The provocative experiments of Bach and Burris (1957) offer the hope that the mechanism of nitrogen fixation will be amenable to critical investigation soon. Two important problems must be solved: (a) the intermediates in the reac-tion must be identified, and (b) the enzymes involved must be purified, so the details of the process can be understood. It seems probable that clarification of the mechanism of ni-trogen fixation will require the employment of new tech-

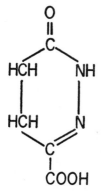

Figure 3. Dihydropyridazinone-5-carboxylic acid.

niques. Perhaps it will require the employment of radioactive nitrogen (nitrogen-13). This isotope, although possessing only a ten minute half-life, can be prepared as extremely high activity nitrogen-13 in the cyclotron, and might serve to trace the incorporation of nitrogen into suspected intermediates, or to allow the detection of minute amounts of fixation in cell-free preparations.

The mechanism of nitrogen fixation has been, and still is, one of the most difficult problems of nitrogen metabolism. The final elucidation of this mechanism will require considerable effort and ingenuity, but it seems likely that the coming decade will see at least the broad outlines of the mechanism, and, perhaps, the final details.

*Summary.* Thus, it can be seen that the nitrogen assimilated by a plant may come from any of several different sources. Amino acids are probably incorporated directly into the pathways of amino acid metabolism, while other organic nitrogen compounds may be degraded before their nitrogen is available to the cell. Ammonia is very likely assimilated initially through the formation of glutamate from $\alpha$-ketoglutarate, but, in some cases, the formation of aspartate, alanine, or some other compound may be quantitatively significant. Both nitrate and molecular nitrogen are reduced to ammonia. Although information is increasing steadily on the chemical steps involved in the assimilation of various forms of nitrogen, much interesting research remains before the pathways are clarified satisfactorily, and their exact significance to cellular nitrogen metabolism is assessed.

### REFERENCES

ADLER, E., DAS, N., EULER, H., AND HEYMAN, V., Compt. rend. trav. lab. Carlsberg Ser. Chim. **22**, 15 (1938).
ANDERSON, A. J. AND SPENCER, D., Australian Jour. Sci. Research **B3**, 414 (1950).
ANDRUS, L. J. AND QUASTEL, J. H., Nature **160**, 222 (1947).
ARNOW, P., OLESON, J. J., AND WILLIAMS, J. H., Am. Jour. Botany **40**, 100 (1953).
ARRINGTON, L. AND SHIVE, J., Soil Sci., **39**, 431 (1935).
BACH, M. K. AND BURRIS, R. H., Federation Proc. **16**, 148 (1957).
BONNER, J., Botan. Gaz. **108**, 267 (1946).
BOYNTON, D., MARGOLIS, D., AND GROSS, C. R., Proc. Amer. Soc. Hort. Sci. **62**, 135 (1953).
BULEN, W. A., Arch. Biochem. Biophys. **62**, 173 (1956).
BURK, D. AND BURRIS, R. H., Ann. Rev. Biochem. **10**, 587 (1941).

BURRIS, R. H. AND WILSON, P. W., Ann. Rev. Biochem. **14,** 685 (1945).

BURRIS, R. H. AND WILSON, P. W., Jour. Bact. **52,** 505 (1946a).

BURRIS, R. H. AND WILSON, P. W., Jour. Biol. Chem. **191,** 295 (1946b).

DAMODARAN, M. AND NAIR, K., Biochem. Jour. **32,** 1064 (1938).

DELWICHE, C. C., Jour. Biol. Chem. **189,** 167 (1951).

EVANS, H. J., Plant Physiol. **29,** 298 (1954).

EVANS, H. J. AND NASON, A., Arch. Biochem. Biophys. **39,** 234 (1952).

EVANS, H. J. AND NASON, A., Plant Physiol. **28,** 233 (1953).

FINCHAM, J. R. S., Jour. Biol. Chem. **182,** 61 (1950).

FINCHAM, J. R. S., Jour. Gen. Microbiol. **5,** 793 (1951).

FINCHAM, J. R. S., Jour. Gen. Microbiol. **11,** 236 (1954).

FREAR, D. S., A Study of the Intermediates Concerned in Nitrate Reduction in Higher Green Plants. Doctoral Dissertation, Ohio State University, 1955.

FREAR, D. S. AND BURRELL, R. C., Anal. Chem. **27,** 1664 (1955).

GEST, H., JUDIS, J., AND PECK, H. D., JR., in *Inorganic Nitrogen Metabolism* (McElroy, W. D. and Glass, B., Eds.), Johns Hopkins Press, Baltimore (1956).

GHOSH, B. P. AND BURRIS, R. H., Soil Sci. **70,** 187 (1950).

HAMILTON, P. B., SHUG, A. L., AND WILSON, P. W., Proc. Natl. Acad. Sci. **43,** 297 (1957).

HEVESY, G., LINDERSTROM-LANG, K., KESTON, A. S., AND OLSEN, C., Compt. rend. trav. lab. Carlsberg Ser. Chim. **23,** 213 (1940).

HEWITT, E. J. AND JONES, E. W., Jour. Pomol. Hort. Sci. **23,** 254 (1947).

HINSVARK, O. N., WITTWER, S. H., AND TUKEY, H. B., Plant Physiol. **28,** 70 (1953).

HOCH, G. E., LITTLE, H. N., AND BURRIS, R. H., Nature **179,** 430 (1957).

HORNER, C. K., BURK, D., ALLISON, F. E., AND SHERMAN, M. S., Jour. Agric. Res. **65,** 173 (1942).

JENSEN, H. L., Proc. Linnean Soc. N. S. Wales **72,** 299 (1947).

KAMEN, M. D. AND GEST, H., Science **109,** 560 (1949).

KEELER, R. F. AND VARNER, J. E., Arch. Biochem. Biophys. **70,** 585 (1957a).

KEELER, R. F. AND VARNER, J. E., Bact. Proc. **112** (1957b).

LEE, S. B. AND WILSON, P. W., Jour. Biol. Chem. **151,** 377 (1943).

LEMOIGNE, M., MONQUILLON, P., AND DESVEAUX, R., Bull. soc. chim. biol. **18,** 868 (1936).

LEMOIGNE, M., MONQUILLON, P., AND DESVEAUX, R., Compt. rend. **204,** 1841 (1937).

LIND, C. J. AND WILSON, P. W., Arch. Biochem. **1,** 59 (1942).

MACVICAR, R. AND BURRIS, R. H., Jour. Biol. Chem. **176,** 511 (1948).

McELROY, W. D. AND NASON, A., Ann. Rev. Plant Physiol. **5,** 1 (1954).

McELROY, W. D. AND SPENCER, D., in *Inorganic Nitrogen Metabolism* (McElroy, W. D. and Glass, B., Eds.), Johns Hopkins Press, Baltimore (1956).

MEDINA, A. AND NICHOLAS, D. J. D., Nature **179,** 533 (1957).

MENDEL, J. L. AND VISSER, D. W., Arch. Biochem. Biophys. **32,** 185 (1951).

MEYER, V. AND SCHULZE, E., Berichte **17,** 1554 (1894).

MICHLIN, D. M., Compt. rend. acad. sci. U.R.S.S. **20,** 149 (1938).

MOLNAR, D. M., BURRIS, R. H., AND WILSON, P. W., Jour. Am. Chem. Soc. **70,** 1713 (1948).

MOZEN, M. M. AND BURRIS, R. H., Biochim. Biophys. Acta **14,** 577 (1954).

MULDER, E. G., Plant and Soil **1,** 94 (1948).

NASON, A. AND EVANS, H. J., Jour. Biol. Chem. **202,** 655 (1953).

NASON, A., ABRAHAM, R. C., AND AVERBACH, B. C., Biochim. Biophys. Acta **15,** 159 (1954).

NETIEN, G. AND BEAUCHESNE, G., Ann. Biol. **30,** 437 (1954).

Nicholas, D. J. D., Nature **179**, 800 (1957).

Nicholas, D. J. D. and Nason, A., Arch. Biochem. Biophys. **51**, 310 (1954).

Nicholas, D. J. D., Nason, A., and McElroy, W. D., Jour. Biol. Chem. **207**, 341 (1954).

Nightingale, G. T., Botan. Rev. **3**, 85 (1937).

Nightingale, G. T., Botan. Rev. **14**, 185 (1948).

Otani, T. T. and Meister, A., Jour. Biol. Chem. **224**, 137 (1957).

Paris, D. and Duhamet, L., Compt. rend. **236**, 169 (1953).

Pearsall, W. H. and Billimoria, M. C., Biochem. Jour. **31**, 1743 (1937).

Ratner, E. I., Kolosov, I. I., Ukhina, S. F., Dobrokhotova, I. N., and Kazuto, O. N., Izvest. Akad. Nauk. S.S.S.R., Ser. Biol. No. **6**, 64, (1956).

Rautanen, N., Acta Chem. Scand. **2**, 127 (1948).

Rautanen, N., Ann. Acad. Sci. Fennicae, Ser. A, II, Chem., No. 33, (1948).

Riker, A. J. and Gutsche, A. E., Am. Jour. Botany **35**, 227 (1948).

Robbins, W. J., Am. Jour. Botany **24**, 243 (1937).

Rosenblum, E. D. and Wilson, P. W., Jour. Bact. **59**, 83 (1950).

Sessions, A. and Shive, J., Soil Sci. **35**, 355 (1933).

Slocum, D. H., Mechanisms of Arsenate Activation in Enzymatic Reactions. Doctoral Dissertation, Ohio State University, 1958.

Shug, A. L., Hamilton, P. B., and Wilson, P. W., in *Inorganic Nitrogen Metabolism* (McElroy, W. D. and Glass, B., Eds.), Johns Hopkins Press, Baltimore (1956).

Silver, W. S. and McElroy, W. D., Arch. Biochem. Biophys. **51**, 379 (1954).

Spoerl, E., Am. Jour. Botany **35**, 88 (1948).

Steward, F. C. and Pollard, J. K., in *Inorganic Nitrogen Metabolism* (McElroy, W. D. and Glass, B., Eds.), Johns Hopkins Press, Baltimore (1956).

Straus, J. and LaRue, C. D., Am. Jour. Botany **41**, 687 (1954).

Takahashi, H. and Nason, A., Biochim. Biophys. Acta **23**, 433 (1957).

Theelin, G. and Beaumont, A., Jour. Am. Soc. Agron. **26**, 1012 (1934).

Vanecko, S. and Varner, J. E., Plant Physiol. **30**, 388 (1955).

Vickery, H. B., Pucher, G., Schoenheimer, R., and Rittenberg, D., Jour. Biol. Chem. **135**, 531 (1940).

Virtanen, A. I. and Tarnanen, J., Biochem. Zeit. **250**, 13 (1932).

Virtanen, A. I. and Arhimo, A. A., Suomen Kemistilehti **B12**, 24 (1939).

Virtanen, A. I. and Linkola, H., Nature **158**, 515 (1946).

Walker, J. B., Proc. Natl. Acad. Sci. **38**, 561 (1952).

Warburg, O. and Negelein, E., Biochem. Zeit. **110**, 66 (1920).

Webster, G. C., Plant Physiol. **29**, 382 (1954).

Webster, G. C. and Varner, J. E., Jour. Biol. Chem. **215**, 91 (1955a).

Webster, G. C., Varner, J. E., and Gansa, A. N., Plant Physiol. **30**, 372 (1955b).

White, P. R., Plant Physiol. **12**, 793 (1937).

Wilson, P. W., *The Biochemistry of Symbiotic Nitrogen Fixation*, Univ. of Wisconsin Press, Madison (1940).

Wilson, P. W., Adv. in Enzymol. **13**, 345 (1952).

Wilson, P. W. and Burris, R. H., Bact. Revs. **11**, 41 (1947).

Wilson, P. W., Umbreit, W. W., and Lee, S. B., Biochem. Jour. **32**, 2984 (1938).

Wilson, R. D. and Waring, E. J., Jour. Austrialian Inst. Agr. Sci. **14**, 141 (1948).

Wyss, O. and Wilson, P. W., Proc. Natl. Acad. Sci. **27**, 162 (1941).

Zelitch, I., Federation Proc. **16**, 276 (1957).

Zelitch, I., Rosenblum, E. D., and Burris, R. H., Jour. Biol. Chem. **191**, 295 (1951).

Zucker, M. and Nason, A., Jour. Biol. Chem. **213**, 463 (1955).

# Chapter 2

# Amino Acid Metabolism

The principal initial products of nitrogen assimilation are amino acids. Extensive determinations of the amino acid composition of various plant proteins (Lugg, 1949; McCalla, 1949; Tristram, 1953) reveal that such proteins are composed of all or many of the following L-amino acids: alanine, arginine, aspartate, cysteine, glutamate, glycine, histidine, hydroxyproline, isoleucine, leucine, lysine, methionine, phenylalanine, proline, serine, threonine, tryptophan, tyrosine, and valine. Comparison of the amino acid composition of plant proteins with the amino acid composition of animal proteins reveals no striking differences in the relative proportions of the various amino acids. A few reports have appeared on the occurrence of unusual amino acids in plant proteins, but they are generally based on insufficient evidence to be accepted as yet. One exception to this, however, is the work of Windsor (1951b) where the evidence seems quite clear that α-aminoadipic acid is a constituent of a water-soluble protein of corn seed.

In contrast to the relative uniformity encountered in the amino acid composition of proteins, the kinds and relative amounts of free amino acids in plant cells exhibit great variation. Among other things, the variations occur as a function of: the species of plant examined, the organ of the plant used for analysis, and the age of the tissue being studied. As the free amino acids are undoubtedly in equilibrium with other carbon compounds in the cell, it would not be surprising if many other factors, both physiological and environmental, influence the content of free amino acids in cells. Some studies on the variations of free amino acids in plants have been performed (Alsopp, 1948; Steward, *et al.*, 1954, 1955), but the results are difficult to interpret as yet in terms of a unified metabolic pattern. Much more information is necessary on the kinetics of formation, breakdown, and utilization of amino acids before we can hope to interpret changes in the levels of these many free amino acids in any sensible manner.

More striking than changes that occur in the relative amounts of the common amino acids, however, have been the numerous discoveries of entirely new amino acids in plant cells. Some, such as citrulline, ornithine, β-alanine, homoserine, α-aminobutyric acid, γ-aminobutyric acid, and α-aminoadipic acid, have also been found in animals, but most of the unusual amino acids have been found only in higher plants or microorganisms. Their detection has been due principally to the use of paper chromatography. Indeed, the finding of many non-protein amino acids was an early product of the paper chromatography of extracts of plant cells (Dent, *et al.*, 1947; Steward and Thompson, 1950; Virtanen, 1955). Continued chromatographic investigation of various plant species has revealed an ever-increasing number of unexpected amino acids. A partial listing of such amino acids is presented in Table IV. Because few of these substances have been found as yet in proteins, a question may be raised as to their function in plants. However, little information is available on either the function or the metabolism of the amino acids contained in Table IV. Ornithine and citrulline apparently act as intermediates in arginine synthesis (Srb and Horowitz, 1944; Kasting and Delwiche, 1955); β-alanine is a constituent of the vitamin, pantothenic acid (Weinstock, *et al.*, 1939); homoserine is an intermediate in threonine synthesis (Black and Wright, 1955); and γ-aminobutyric acid may be a product of the metabolism of glutamic acid (Schales, *et al.*, 1946). Thus, it would not be surprising if the remaining amino acids listed in Table IV turn out to be constituents of various complex nitrogenous substances, or intermediates in the synthesis and breakdown of amino acids, alkaloids, growth regulators, or other important nitrogenous plant constituents. It would also not be surprising if some of these unusual amino acids, now that they have been identified in plants, would be found in the non-protein extracts of animal cells. Undoubtedly, the judicious employment of paper chromatography will result in the discovery of many more of these interesting compounds.

In addition to the amino acids discussed above, Virtanen and Miettinen (1953) have reported that a group of "bound" amino acids occur in the soluble nitrogen fraction of pea and alder. This fraction contains compounds of amino acids with sugars. This observation is of particular interest in view of the finding of Borsook, *et al.* (1955) that amino acid-sugar compounds occur in animal tissues and promote the incorporation of both iron and amino acids into reticulocyte hemoglobin. It will be of interest to learn more concerning the nature and possible function of such compounds in plants.

## METABOLISM OF THE AMINO GROUP
### OF AMINO ACIDS

We have already discussed (Chapter 1) one way in which an amino group can be added to or removed from an amino acid. In the case of glutamic acid, a reductive amination or oxidative deamination occurs which directly adds ammonia to or removes it from the acid. The question has long been raised as to whether a similar process participates in the synthesis or breakdown of the other amino acids in a plant cell. The possibility that such a process is operative in the oxidative deamination of other amino acids was raised by the finding of an l-amino acid oxidase in *Neurospora* (Bender and Krebs, 1950; Thayer and Horowitz, 1951). Studies have now indicated, however, that a direct amination or deamination may not be of general importance in the metabolism of most other amino acids in higher plants. Wilson, *et al.* (1954) attempted unsuccessfully to demonstrate significant reductive amination of various keto acids with $N^{15}H_3$. Likewise, Rogers (1955a) showed oxidative deamination of almost all amino acids to be either very slow or nonexistent. A comparison of the results of Rogers (1955a) on squash extracts with those of Thayer and Horowitz (1951) on *Neurospora* extracts is presented in Table V. There is little doubt of the difference in activity of the two preparations.

TABLE IV

Non-protein Amino Acids Found in Plants

| Amino acid | Source | Reference |
|---|---|---|
| β-Alanine | Apple | Hulme and Arthington, 1950. |
| Alliin (S-Allyl cysteine sulfoxide) | Garlic | Stoll and Seebeck, 1947. |
| *Allo*-4-hydroxyproline | *Santalum album* | Radhakrishnan and Giri, 1954. |
| α-Aminoadipic acid | Pea, corn | Berg, *et al.*, 1954; Windsor, 1951a. |
| α-Aminobutyric acid | Various plants | Dent, *et al.*, 1947. |
| γ-Aminobutyric acid | Various plants | Dent, *et al.*, 1947. |
| γ-Amino-β-methylenebutyric acid | Tulip | Fowden and Done, 1953. |
| α-Aminopimelic acid | *Asplenium septentrionale* | Virtanen and Berg, 1954. |
| Azetidine-2-carboxylic acid | Lily-of-the-valley | Fowden, 1955. |
| Canavanine | Soybean | Kitagawa and Monobe, 1933. |
| Citrulline | Watermelon | Wada, 1930. |
| 4,5-Dehydropipecolic acid (4,5-Dehydropiperidine-2-carboxylic acid) | *Baikiaea plurijuga* | King, *et al.*, 1950. |
| 3,4-Dehydropiperidine-3-carboxylic acid | Betel seeds | Jahn, 1891. |
| 3,4-Dihydroxyphenylalanine | Various plants | Guggenheim, 1913. |
| Djenkolic acid (Cysteine formaldehyde thioacetal) | *Pithecolobium Lobatum* | van Veen and Hyman, 1935. |
| γ-Glutamylethylamide | Tea leaves | Sakato, 1950. |
| Homoserine | Pea | Miettinen, *et al.*, 1953. |
| γ-Hydroxy-α-aminopimelic acid | *Asplenium septentrionale* | Virtanen, *et al.*, 1954. |
| γ-Hydroxyglutamic acid | *Phlox decusata* | Virtanen and Hietala, 1955. |
| 4-Hydroxypipecolic acid | *Acacia pentadena* | Virtanen and Kari, 1955. |
| 5-Hydroxypipecolic acid | *Rhapis flabelliformis* | Virtanen and Kari, 1954. |
| γ-Methyleneglutamic acid | *Arachis hypogaea* | Done and Fowden, 1952. |

| | | |
|---|---|---|
| γ-Methylglutamic acid | *Phyllitis scolopendrium* | Virtanen and Berg, 1955. |
| γ-Methyl-γ-Hydroxyglutamic acid | *Adiantum* species | Grobbelaar, *et al.*, 1955. |
| γ-Methyl-γ-Hydroxyproline | Apple | Urbach, 1955; Hulme and Steward, 1955. |
| γ-Methylproline | Apple | Hulme and Arthington, 1954. |
| N-Methylguvasin (N-Methyl-3,4-Dehydropiperidine-3-carboxylic acid) | Areca seeds | Wohl and Johnson, 1907. |
| N-Methyl tryptophan | *Abrus precatorius* | Yoshida and Fukuyama, 1941. |
| S-Methyl cysteine | Bean | Thompson, *et al.*, 1956. |
| S-Methyl cysteine sulfoxide | Turnip roots, cabbage | Morris and Thompson, 1956; Synge and Wood, 1956. |
| Mimosine β-[N-(3-Hydroxypyridone-4)]-α-aminopropionic acid | *Mimosa pudica* | Mascre, 1937. |
| Ornithine and N-acetylornithine | *Asplenium nidus* | Virtanen and Linko, 1955. |
| Piperidine-2-carboxylic acid (Pipecolic acid) | Various plants | Zaccharius, *et al.*, 1952. |
| Taurine (2-Aminoethanesulfonic acid) | Various plants | Dent, 1948. |

The observation of Zelitch (1957) that extracts of tobacco leaves catalyze a DPN-linked oxidation of several amino acids (notably of aspartate, glutamine, asparagine, and glycine) suggests that at least a few amino acids may undergo metabolism by direct removal of their amino group. It will be of interest to learn how important these reactions are to the amino acid metabolism not only of tobacco leaves, but of plants in general.

In plants, the addition or removal of the amino groups of the great majority of amino acids proceeds by the process of transamination. Transamination is a chemical reaction in which an amino group is transferred from one molecule to another without the intermediate formation of free ammonia. It was first demonstrated by Herbst and Engel (1934) with boiling solutions of amino and keto acids, and proceeds as follows:

$$R_1-\underset{\underset{NH_2}{|}}{\overset{\overset{H}{|}}{C}}-COOH \ + \ R_2-\overset{\overset{O}{\|}}{C}-COOH \ \rightleftharpoons$$

$$R_1-\overset{\overset{O}{\|}}{C}-COOH \ + \ R_2-\underset{\underset{NH_2}{|}}{\overset{\overset{H}{|}}{C}}-COOH$$

Several years later, the pioneering studies of Braunstein and Kritzmann (1937) and of Cohen (1939) demonstrated the occurrence of enzyme-catalyzed transaminations in a wide variety of organisms, including plants. Early work with a number of plant preparations (Kritzmann, 1939; Virtanen and Laine, 1938; Albaum and Cohen, 1943; Leonard and Burris, 1947) established the widespread occurrence of the following transamination reactions:

Glutamate + oxalacetate $\rightleftharpoons$ $\alpha$-ketoglutarate + aspartate

Glutamate + pyruvate $\rightleftharpoons$ $\alpha$-ketoglutarate + alanine

Aspartate + pyruvate $\rightleftharpoons$ oxalacetate + alanine

TABLE V

Specificity of Amino Acid Oxidases of Neurospora and of Squash

| Amino acid | Microliters $O_2$ consumption/hr./mg. protein | |
| --- | --- | --- |
| | *Neurospora* | Squash |
| Alanine | 102 | 0.6 |
| Arginine | 179 | 0.5 |
| Aspartate | 0 | 0.2 |
| Cysteine | 272 | 2.5 |
| Glycine | 0 | 0 |
| Histidine | 448 | 0 |
| Leucine | 320 | 0 |
| Methionine | 170 | 0 |
| Phenylalanine | 339 | 0.3 |
| Proline | 0 | 0.3 |
| Serine | 0 | 0 |
| Threonine | 0 | 0 |
| Tryptophan | 138 | 0 |
| Tyrosine | 390 | 0 |
| Valine | 61 | 0 |

Further investigation has shown that a number of transamination reactions, involving all of the common amino acids, can be demonstrated in plants. Stumpf (1951) found transamination involving γ-aminobutyrate, leucine, isoleucine, valine, and norvaline. Miettinen and Virtanen (1953b) extended the list to include transamination between α-ketoglutarate and both γ-aminobutyrate and citrulline. Fowden and Done (1953) demonstrated transamination between glycine and α-ketoglutarate, and Wilson, King, and Burris (1954), in a comprehensive study, demonstrated transamination between glutamate and seventeen different amino acids. Transamination is also important to the metabolism of the non-protein amino acids occurring in plants. Fowden and Done (1953) have demonstrated transamination of α-ketoglutarate and both γ-methyleneglutamate and γ-methylglutamate. The recent finding of Meister (1955) that transamination is involved in the metabolism of most amino acids and amides in animals and bacteria indicates that further examples of transamination involving similar amino acids in plants will be forthcoming soon.

The importance of transamination to amino acid metabolism makes it necessary for us to understand the mechanism by which enzymatic transamination takes place. Unfortunately, pure transaminase preparations have not yet been obtained, so the important question of whether the various transamination reactions are catalyzed by a few or by a large number of enzymes cannot be answered. Preparations from different organisms have been purified sufficiently, however, to show that pyridoxal phosphate is a necessary cofactor for transamination. Information on the manner in which pyridoxal phosphate may function has been obtained by Metzler and Snell (1952). They have demonstrated that transamination reactions of the type:

pyridoxal + $\alpha$-amino acid $\rightleftharpoons$ pyridoxamine + $\alpha$-keto acid

proceed non-enzymatically in aqueous solution at 100°C. and pH 3 to 8 in the presence of metal ions. Investigation of the structural features of pyridoxal necessary for activity leads to the conclusion that non-enzymatic transamination proceeds through the intermediate formation of a Schiff base as depicted in Figure 4. The enzymatic reaction presumably also proceeds through the intermediate formation of a Schiff base (Metzler and Snell, 1952), and it is possible that the enzyme molecule replaces the metal ion. While non-enzymatic trans-

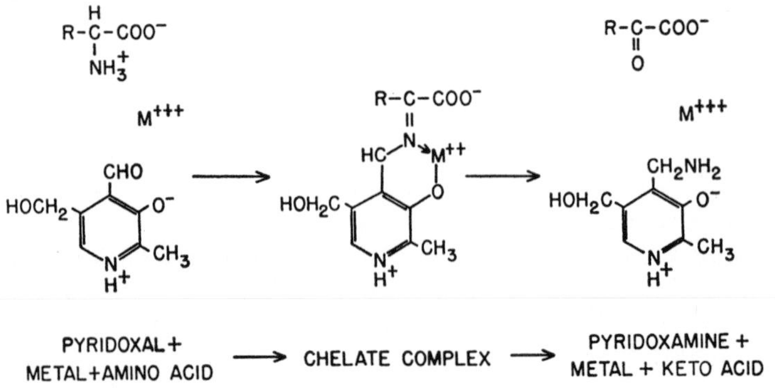

PYRIDOXAL +
METAL + AMINO ACID  ⟶  CHELATE COMPLEX  ⟶  PYRIDOXAMINE +
METAL + KETO ACID

Figure 4. Formation of a chelate complex during non-enzymatic transamination.

amination proceeds in the presence of free pyridoxal, enzymatic transamination requires pyridoxal phosphate, and all evidence points to a function of the phosphate group in the binding of pyridoxal to the transaminase.

## PATHWAYS OF THE BIOSYNTHESIS
## AND DEGRADATION OF AMINO ACIDS

Our knowledge of the manner in which amino acids are built up from simple precursors and ammonia has increased greatly in the past few years. Modern biochemistry has shown that the biosynthesis of a particular substance generally does not proceed by a simple reversal of its breakdown. Instead, new and unexpected pathways of biosynthesis have been uncovered which often possess ingenious energy-conserving reactions. Amino acid biosynthesis is no exception, in that the pathways followed during biosynthesis differ completely in many cases from those of amino acid degradation. For this knowledge of how amino acids are formed, we are chiefly indebted to an imposing array of experiments which have been performed with microorganisms. Two techniques, used either singly or in combination, have resulted in the discovery of a large number of pathways of amino acid synthesis. These techniques are:

a. The use of mutant strains of *Neurospora crassa* and *Escherichia coli*, in which various steps in the biosynthetic pathways are blocked, and intermediates accumulate (Davis, 1955a,b,c).

b. The use of $C^{14}$-labeled metabolites and the direct isolation of suspected intermediates, or the use of "isotopic competition" in which an unlabeled intermediate is allowed to compete with a labeled metabolite, and the extent of the dilution of incorporation of the metabolite determined. Likewise, by the use of $C^{14}$-labeled amino acids, great advances have been made in our knowledge of how the carbon skeletons of various amino acids are degraded.

A thorough discussion of the results obtained by these techniques would now encompass a volume much larger than the present review. Therefore, only a brief summary of the pathways involved in amino acid synthesis and degradation is presented below, together with information on how the pathway is supported by experimental evidence.

*Glutamate, aspartate, alanine, and γ-aminobutyrate.* In any discussion of amino acid metabolism, glutamate must, of necessity, occupy a key position for three reasons:

a. As indicated in Chapter 1, studies with $N^{15}H_3$ and with *Neurospora* mutants demonstrate that the formation of glutamate by the reductive amination of α-ketoglutarate can constitute the major gateway for the entrance of ammonia into the nitrogenous constituents of the plant.

b. Glutamate is apparently capable of transamination with the keto acid corresponding to almost any known amino acid. Thus, because the addition or removal of the amino group by transamination often constitutes the final step in amino acid degradation, glutamate and α-ketoglutarate occupy key positions as amino group donors or acceptors during the metabolism of other amino acids.

c. It is now known that the intact glutamate molecule serves as a precursor for a number of other amino acids, including γ-aminobutyrate, proline, hydroxyproline, ornithine, citrulline, and arginine.

The synthesis and breakdown of glutamate by the action of the enzyme, glutamic dehydrogenase, has already been discussed (Chapter 1). All evidence points to this enzyme mediating the principal pathway either of glutamate synthesis from α-ketoglutarate and ammonia or of glutamate degradation to these substances. In addition to its breakdown following a primary deamination, glutamate is also metabolized in some plants by a decarboxylation to γ-aminobutyric acid. The enzyme catalyzing this reaction has been found in cell-free extracts of many plants, but occurs especially in squash (Schales, *et al.*, 1946; Beevers, 1951; Miettinen and Virtanen, 1953a). Glutamic decarboxylase has been purified partially by Hood (1954), and requires pyridoxal phosphate as a cofactor. The activity of this enzyme may be reflected in the widespread distribution of γ-aminobutyrate in plants, although clear evidence that γ-aminobutyrate is formed only by glutamate decarboxylation is lacking. The enzyme does not decarboxylate aspartate, and no firm evidence for the occurrence of an aspartic decarboxylase is at hand. It has been observed, however, that wheat germ extracts catalyze an incorporation of $C^{14}O_2$ into aspartate in the presence of β-alanine (Webster and Varner, 1955), indicating the possible activity of such an enzyme.

The further degradation of γ-aminobutyrate has been studied only slightly. The author has observed that the carbon of $C^{14}$-γ-aminobutyrate is incorporated into various Krebs cycle acids in wheat germ extracts, but that it accumulates almost entirely in succinate if malonate is present in the system. This suggests that γ-aminobutyrate can be metabolized in the following manner:

γ-aminobutyrate → succinic semialdehyde → succinate

Whether other metabolic pathways are available to γ-aminobutyrate is not yet clear.

Like glutamate, both aspartate and alanine arise directly from the Krebs cycle. At least two pathways for their formation are apparent (Chapter 1):

a. Aspartate and alanine are formed by transamination reactions between glutamate and either oxalacetate or pyruvate.

b. Aspartate can be formed by a direct amination of fumarate catalyzed by the enzyme, aspartase. Likewise, it is possible that alanine can be formed in plants by a reductive amination of pyruvate. Unfortunately, the extent that these reactions participate in aspartate or alanine synthesis is not known. It is suspected, however, that amino acid formation by transamination is more important.

*Proline and hydroxyproline.* In contrast to the simple nature of the reactions leading to the formation of glutamate, aspartate, alanine, and γ-aminobutyrate, the formation of proline and hydroxyproline is relatively complex. These amino acids arise from glutamate by the reactions depicted in Figure 5. Mutant strains of *E. coli* occur in which the conversion of glutamate to its semialdehyde, and the conversion of the semialdehyde to proline are blocked (Davis, 1950; Vogel and Davis, 1952). The latter mutant excretes glutamic-γ-semialdehyde into the medium, where it spontaneously equilibrates with Δ'-pyrroline-5-carboxylic acid. Under physiological conditions, the equilibrium favors the formation of the cyclic material. Similar mutants of *Neurospora crassa* and *Torulopsis utilis* have been found (Vogel and Bonner, 1954). Further evidence for the pathway shown in Figure 5 has been

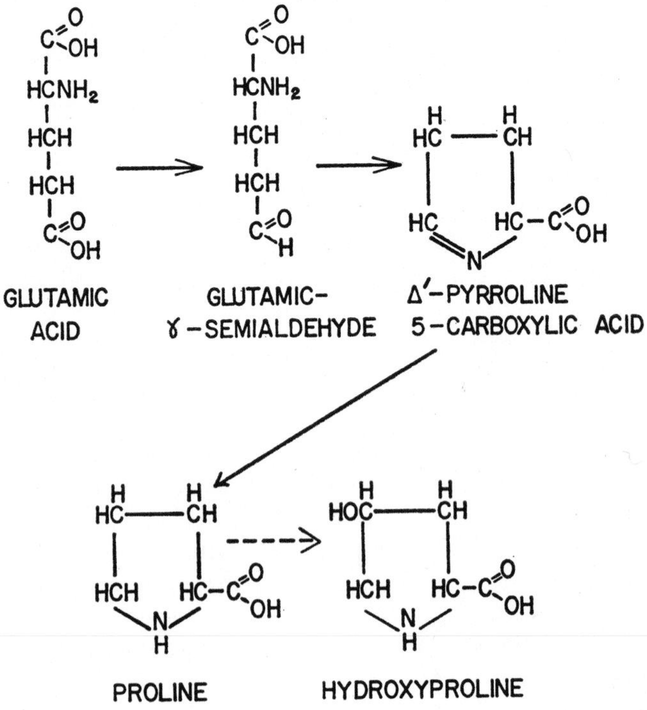

Figure 5. Pathway of conversion of glutamate to proline and hydroxyproline.

obtained by tracer experiments in which the postulated intermediates have been shown to dilute the incorporation of precursor into proline. Although isotopic experiments (Stetten
and Schoenheimer, 1944) have shown hydroxyproline to be
formed from proline in mammals, its mode of formation in
plants is not yet known.

*Ornithine, citrulline, arginine and the urea cycle.* In addition to serving as a precursor of proline and hydroxyproline,
glutamate is also transformed into ornithine, citrulline, and
arginine. Like proline synthesis, ornithine formation in *Neurospora* and *Torulopsis* (Vogel and Bonner, 1954; Abelson
and Vogel, 1955) proceeds via glutamic-γ-semialdehyde (Figure 6). The conversion of the semialdehyde to ornithine is
brought about by a transamination from glutamate, and the
enzyme catalyzing this reaction, ornithine transaminase, has
been isolated from *Neurospora* (Fincham, 1953). In contrast
to these organisms, *E. coli* has been shown by Vogel (1953) to
utilize a series of acetylated intermediates, beginning with
N-acetyl glutamate (Figure 6). Mutants possessing blocks at
each of the steps in the glutamate-ornithine conversion have
been obtained, and two of the intermediates, N-acetyl ornithine and N-acetyl glutamic-γ-semialdehyde accumulate in the
medium surrounding the appropriately blocked mutants.
Tracer experiments with N-acetyl glutamate and N-acetyl
ornithine have provided further evidence of their activity as
ornithine precursors (Vogel, *et al.*, 1953). The dichotomy observed here raises a question as to the manner in which ornithine is formed in other plants. No conclusive information is
available, but the finding of N-acetyl ornithine in higher
plants by Virtanen and Linko (1953) suggests that the pathway utilized by *E. coli* should be considered and subjected to
appropriate experiments.

The further transformation of ornithine to citrulline and
arginine in plants appears to follow the course of these same
reactions in the classical urea cycle of mammals (Figure 7).
Indeed, evidence for the complete series of reactions of the
urea cycle has been found in *Neurospora* by Srb and Horowitz (1944) and in higher plants by Kasting and Delwiche

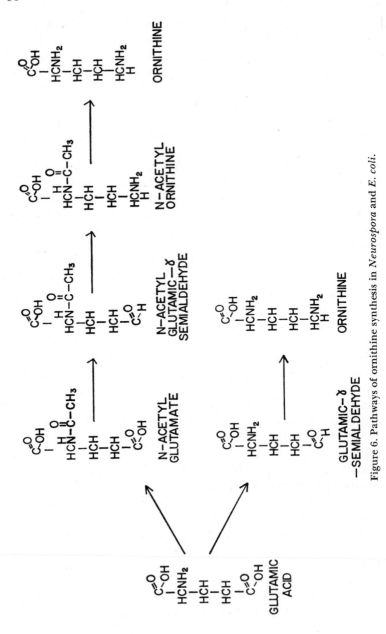

Figure 6. Pathways of ornithine synthesis in *Neurospora* and *E. coli.*

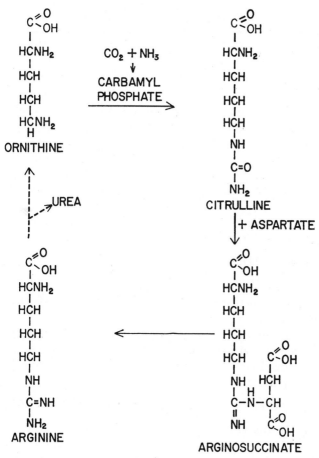

Figure 7. Relationships of ornithine, citrulline, and arginine in the ornithine cycle.

(1955). The conversion of ornithine to citrulline is of considerable interest in that it involves the participation of a hitherto unsuspected phosphorylated intermediate, carbamyl phosphate (Jones, *et al.*, 1955). The transformation of citrulline to arginine likewise produces an interesting intermediate, arginosuccinate (Ratner, *et al.*, 1953). The enzyme catalyzing arginosuccinate formation has been found in *Neurospora* and yeast, while the enzyme catalyzing arginine formation from arginosuccinate occurs in *E. coli*, peas, jack beans, and *Chlorella* (Davison and Elliott, 1952; Walker, 1952; Walker and Myers, 1953).

The degradation of ornithine, citrulline, and arginine can be summarized briefly. One pathway of arginine degradation is the classical mammalian mechanism to ornithine and either urea or $CO_2 + NH_3$. Ornithine, in turn, can be degraded, through loss of both amino groups, to $\alpha$-ketoglutarate. A second pathway, catalyzed by arginine desimidase, results in the hydrolysis of arginine to citrulline plus ammonia. The fate of citrulline is less clear. In some microorganisms and higher plants, an enzyme system, citrulline phosphorylase (Knivett, 1954), occurs which degrades citrulline to ornithine with the simultaneous formation of adenosine triphosphate:

$$\text{citrulline} + \text{ADP} + P_i \rightleftharpoons \text{ornithine} + NH_3 + CO_2 + \text{ATP}$$

Whether this interesting reaction operates in all plants, and whether it constitutes an important pathway of citrulline metabolism is not known.

*Homoserine and threonine.* Like glutamate, aspartate acts as a precursor of certain other amino acids. An enzyme, aspartokinase (Black and Gray, 1953), catalyzes the phosphorylation of aspartate by the reaction:

$$\text{Aspartate} + \text{ATP} \rightleftharpoons \beta\text{-aspartyl phosphate} + \text{ADP}$$

Aspartyl phosphate is then transformed into homoserine and threonine by a series of reactions (Figure 8). The exact manner in which homoserine itself is converted to threonine is not yet clear, but the overall reaction requires both ATP and pyridoxal phosphate. The transformation may involve an activated intermediate, as hydroxylamine reacts with homoserine in the presence of ATP and the homoserine-threonine enzyme preparation to form a hydroxamic acid (Nisman, *et al.*, 1954). Watanabe and Shimura (1956) have reported that homoserine and ATP react to form o-phosphohomoserine, which is then transformed into threonine with the liberation of phosphate, but the manner of this transformation is still not understood.

In the case of the reactions leading to homoserine formation, the enzymes catalyzing each step have been isolated and their action studied in detail (Black and Wright, 1955a,b). The reactions catalyzed by these enzymes (Figure 8) are in complete conformity with the evidence obtained with *Neurospora* mutants (Teas, *et al.*, 1948), and with isotopically-labeled substrates (Abelson, 1954).

*The branched-chain amino acids: leucine, isoleucine, and valine.* Studies with mutants of *Neurospora* and *E. coli* have shed some light on the manner in which the branched-chain amino acids are formed. Nevertheless, the picture is far from complete. Results of investigations using both isotopes and mutants have established that the synthesis of these amino acids is fairly complex. Isotopic experiments have demonstrated that α-ketobutyrate and pyruvate (or compounds derived from these substances) act as precursors of isoleucine (Adelberg, 1955). In a similar fashion, valine may be formed from pyruvate, possibly by a pinacol-like rearrangement. Leucine is seemingly formed in yeast from valine and acetate (Strassman, *et al.*, 1956). The actual pathways and mechanisms in these syntheses, however, have not been clearly established.

Our knowledge of the manner in which branched-chain amino acids are degraded has been elucidated in considerable detail (Figure 9), and the enzymes involved have been isolated and characterized to a great extent (Coon, 1955). This advance has been due almost entirely to the skillful interpretation of data obtained by the study of the products formed from suitably labeled amino acids and their suspected degradation products. Most of our information on branched-chain amino acid degradation has been obtained through the study of mammals, but recent studies have indicated similar pathways in plants. Thus, studies in the author's laboratory with $C^{14}$-leucine have shown that leucine is degraded by guayule seedlings to α-ketoisocaproate, isovalerate, and dimethylacrylate. Johnston, *et al.* (1954) have demonstrated the further degradation of dimethylacrylate to acetyl-CoA by the pathway illustrated in Figure 9. It would not be surprising, therefore,

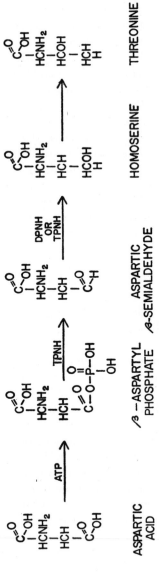

Figure 8. Conversion of aspartate to homoserine and threonine.

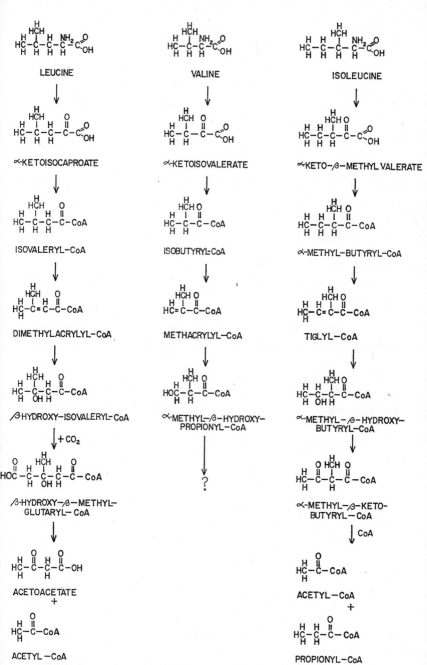

Figure 9. Pathways of degradation of leucine, isoleucine, and valine.

if valine and isoleucine were also degraded in plants by schemes similar to those shown in Figure 9.

*Lysine, methionine, cysteine.* Little is known about the synthesis or degradation of these amino acids in plants. Certain lysine-requiring mutants of *Neurospora* are able to utilize α-aminoadipic acid instead of lysine (Mitchell and Houlahan, 1948). Furthermore, $C^{14}$-α-aminoadipic acid is converted into lysine by *Neurospora* (Windsor, 1951). The successive requirements of various mutants are explainable by the following biosynthetic pathway:

$$\alpha\text{-aminoadipate} \rightarrow \alpha\text{-aminoadipic-semialdehyde} \rightarrow \text{lysine}$$

Mutants of *Neurospora* which require compounds prior to α-aminoadipate have not been studied extensively, so little can be said concerning simpler precursors. It is interesting to note that in most bacteria and in the blue-green algae, α-aminoadipate is not a precursor of lysine. Instead, the first recognizable precursor is diaminopimelic acid (Davis, 1952; Dewey and Work, 1952).

The early steps in lysine degradation in plants have been elucidated by a study of the products formed from $C^{14}$-lysine. In both higher plants (Lowy, 1952; Grobbelaar and Steward, 1953) and *Neurospora* (Schweet, *et al.*, 1954), lysine is converted to pipecolic acid (piperidine-2-carboxylic acid). Experiments with *Neurospora* support the following sequence:

$$\text{lysine} \rightarrow \Delta'\text{-dehydropipecolate} \rightarrow \text{pipecolate}$$

The route of further degradation of pipecolate in plants is unknown. In mammals, pipecolate is degraded to α-aminoadipate and thence finally to α-ketoglutarate (Rothstein and Miller, 1954), but experiments with *Neurospora* do not provide evidence for a similar pathway in plants.

As is the case with lysine, there is little concrete information on the formation and breakdown of methionine and cysteine in plants. Studies with *Neurospora* mutants have shown the pathway of methionine synthesis from sulfate probably goes through cysteine. Mutants blocked between cysteine and methionine provide evidence for homocysteine and cystathionine being intermediates, but the detailed metabolic pathway has not been elucidated satisfactorily as yet.

*Glycine and serine.* The early labeling of glycolic acid and glycine during photosynthesis in the presence of $C^{14}O_2$ (Benson and Calvin, 1950) indicates a close metabolic relationship between these substances. Moreover, Tolbert and Cohan (1954) have demonstrated that plants readily convert $C^{14}$-glycolate to $C^{14}$-glycine. This conversion undoubtedly proceeds through the intermediary formation of glyoxylate, as Tolbert, *et al.* (1949) have demonstrated the conversion of glycolate to glyoxylate by green plants. Since glyoxylate is capable of transaminating with glutamate, the following pathway is evident:

$$\text{Glycolate} \xrightarrow{-2H} \text{Glyoxylate} \xrightarrow{+NH_2} \text{Glycine}$$

Information on the manner of formation of glycolate has been obtained by Weissbach and Horecker (1955). They find that a soluble extract of spinach leaves (which is capable of incorporating $C^{14}O_2$ into phosphoglyceric acid in the presence of ribose-5-phosphate) is able to incorporate the carbon of 1-$C^{14}$-ribose-5-phosphate into glycine. Eighty per cent of the radioactivity occurs in the methyl carbon of the glycine molecule. As the spinach extracts contain pentose phosphate isomerase and transketolase, these observations can be explained by the scheme illustrated in Figure 10. The degradation of glycine to simpler substances undoubtedly proceeds through glyoxylate also. The oxidative decarboxylation of glyoxylate to formate appears to be the most likely pathway of glycine degradation.

An important pathway of glycine metabolism is the conversion of glycine to serine. That such a relationship exists in plants was suspected when mutants of *E. coli* were found which have a nutritional requirement that can be satisfied by either glycine or serine (Roepke, *et al.*, 1944). Racusen (1953) observed that soybean leaves readily convert $C^{14}$-glycine to $C^{14}$-serine. The mechanism of this conversion has been studied extensively in animals. The conversion involves the participation of a tetrahydrofolic acid cofactor (Kisliuk and Sa-

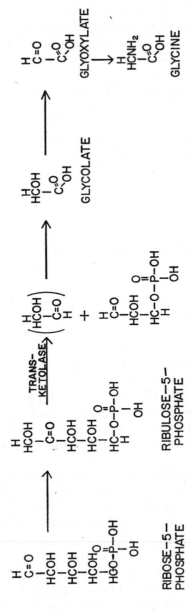

Figure 10. Formation of glycine from ribose-5-phosphate.

kami, 1954), and results from the condensation of an "active formate" (apparently a formyl group attached to a tetrahydrofolic acid cofactor) with a molecule of glycine (Figure 11). If a similar mechanism occurs in plants, then the "active formate" probably arises from glycine also (Figure 11). Evidence in favor of a mechanism like that illustrated in Figure 11 has been obtained by Tolbert (1955). When $C^{14}$-formate is fed to barley leaves, the formate carbon is incorporated into the $\beta$-carbon of serine. Tolbert's data also indicate the absence of a direct pathway between serine and glyceric acid, an important observation in regard to both the synthesis and breakdown of serine. At present, the principal pathway of serine metabolism appears to involve glycine.

*Histidine.* Our knowledge of the pathways involved in the biosynthesis of ring-containing amino acids rests almost entirely on interpretations of the behavior of various mutant forms of microorganisms, in which different steps in the biosynthetic pathways are blocked. A case in point is histidine. A series of histidine-requiring mutants of *Neurospora* have been isolated and found to fall into five groups (Haas, *et al.*, 1952). Certain of these mutants accumulate compounds which have been identified as histidinol phosphate, imidazole acetol phosphate, and imidazole glycerol phosphate (Ames and Mitchell, 1955). In addition, histidinol, imidazole glycerol, and imidazole acetol accumulate, presumably through the

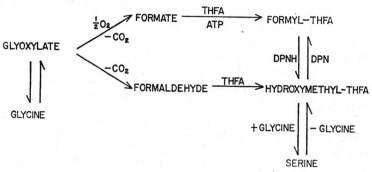

Figure 11. Mechanism of glycine-serine conversion.

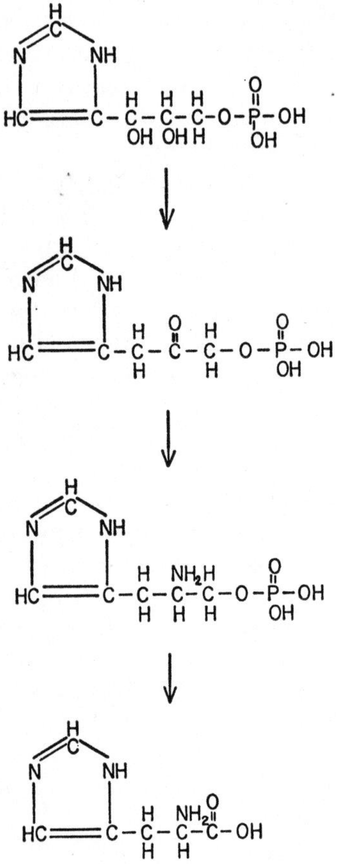

IMIDAZOLE GLYCEROL PHOSPHATE

IMIDAZOLE ACETOL PHOSPHATE

HISTIDINOL PHOSPHATE

HISTIDINE

Figure 12. Pathway of histidine biosynthesis.

degradation of the respective phosphate compounds (Ames, *et al.*, 1953). On the basis of genetic studies, the reactions shown in Figure 12 have been postulated as the final steps in histidine synthesis (Ames, 1955). Certain evidence in favor of this sequence has accumulated. For example, an enzyme has been isolated from *Neurospora* (Ames, 1955) which catalyzes the reaction:

$$\text{Imidazole acetol phosphate} + \text{glutamate} \rightleftharpoons \text{histidinol phosphate} + \alpha\text{-ketoglutarate}$$

A second enzyme has been found which converts imidazole glycerol phosphate to imidazol acetol phosphate, while a third, derived from *E. coli*, oxidizes histidinol to histidine in the presence of DPN (Adams, 1954). Unfortunately, our knowledge of the manner of formation of the imidazole ring is very scanty. Isotopic experiments (Levy and Coon, 1952) have indicated that the five carbon chain of histidine is not derived from glutamate or acetate, but instead may be derived, fairly directly, from glucose. The remaining carbon in the histidine ring comes from formate (Levy and Coon, 1951). None of the ring carbons seem to be derived directly from glycine. Some pathways of histidine degradation in bacteria are presented in Figure 13. It is not yet known whether any of these interesting transformations occur in other plants.

*Tryptophan.* Like histidine, our knowledge of tryptophan biosynthesis is far from complete. Only the final step in the sequence of synthetic reactions is known with certainty. It has been shown (Umbreit, *et al.*, 1946; Yanofsky, 1952) that this final step is:

$$\text{indole} + \text{serine} \rightarrow \text{tryptophan} + H_2O$$

Tryptophan desmolase, the enzyme catalyzing this reaction, has been isolated from microorganisms, and shown to require pyridoxal phosphate for its activity. The mode of formation of the indole ring, however, is not at all clear. Evidence exists relating anthranilic acid, nicotinic acid, or phenylalanine in indole synthesis, but all of these substances may be transformed extensively before a precursor on the actual biosynthetic pathway is produced. The possibility exists that indole is formed from the same intermediates (shikimic acid, for example) that constitute the early steps in the biosynthesis of phenylalanine and tyrosine (see below), but unequivocal evidence for such a relationship is lacking.

Tryptophan can be degraded by any of a number of possible pathways. Of greatest interest in plants is its conversion to the auxin, indoleacetic acid. The potential importance of tryptophan to indoleacetic acid formation was established by Thimann (1952), who observed that the production of indoleacetic acid by *Rhizopus* depends upon the presence of trypto-

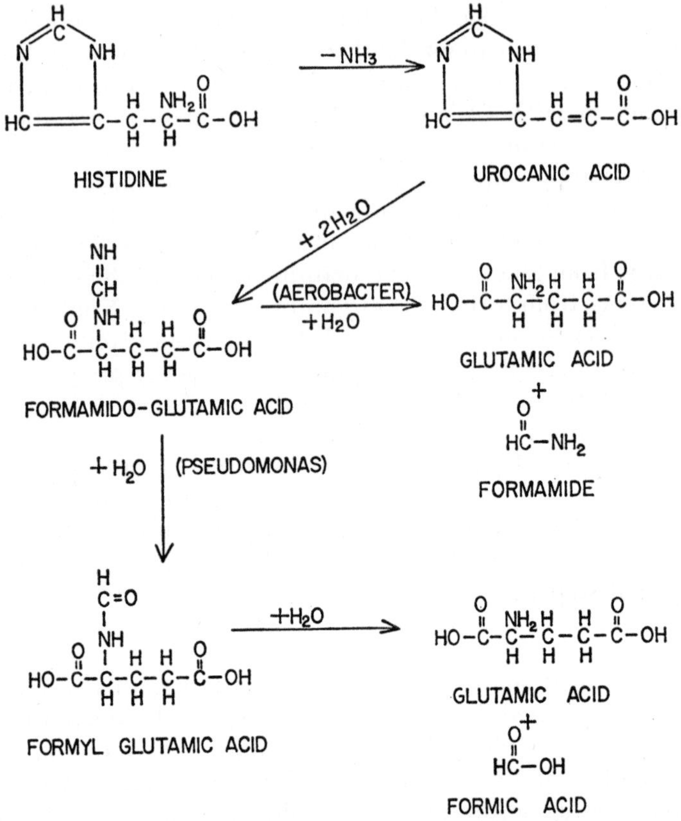

Figure 13. Pathway of histidine degradation.

phan. Numerous subsequent studies confirmed the conversion of tryptophan to indoleacetic acid. There are two possible pathways of indoleacetic acid formation from tryptophan (Figure 14), and evidence supporting each has appeared. Tryptamine occurs in *Acacia* (White, 1944), and is converted to indoleacetic acid by pineapple leaf preparations (Gordon and Nieva, 1948). In contrast, spinach leaves will not metabolize tryptamine, but will convert indolepyruvic acid to indoleacetic acid (Wildman, *et al.*, 1947). Pineapple leaves, which convert tryptamine to indoleacetate, also convert indolepyruvate to indoleacetate. It appears that either or both pathways may be operative in different plants. All preparations convert indoleacetaldehyde to indoleacetate, and indoleacetaldehyde may well be an immediate precursor of indoleacetate. It should be remembered, however, that none of these pathways

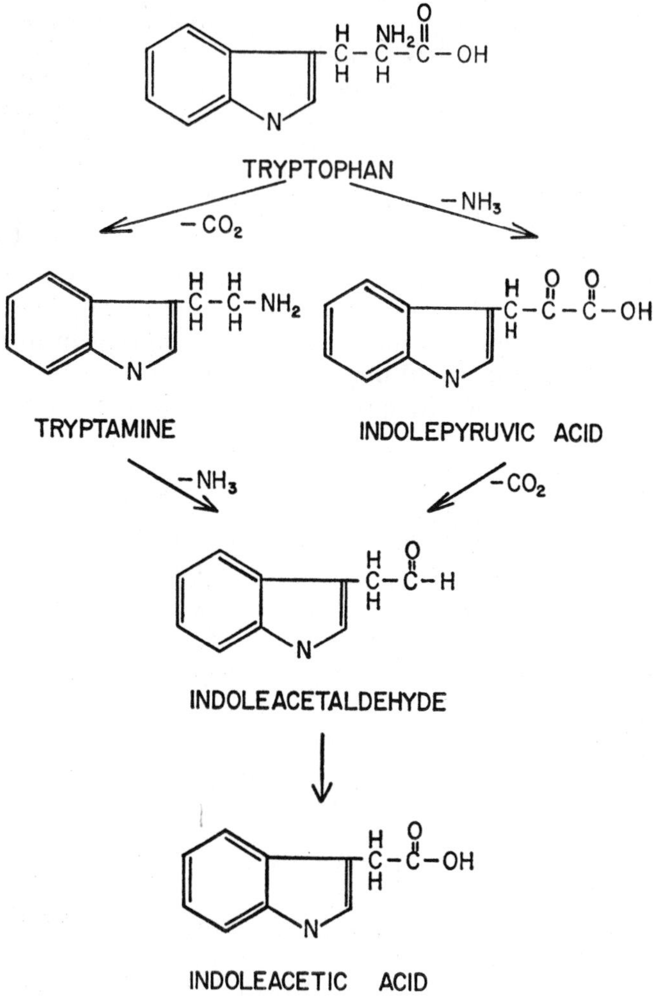

Figure 14. Pathway of conversion of tryptophan to indoleacetic acid.

has been unequivocally established as the major route of indoleacetate synthesis in plants, and Greenberg, *et al.* (1957) have suggested that indole may combine with glyoxylate to form indoleglycolate, which is subsequently converted to indoleacetate. It would seem that good isotopic investigations are badly needed in this area. The degradation of indoleacetate has been subjected to considerable study, but is not completely understood. Tang and Bonner (1947) showed that pea extracts oxidatively decarboxylate indoleacetate with retention of the indole ring. In a similar reaction catalyzed by bean extracts, Wagenknecht and Burris (1949) found that the oxidation product reacted with 2,4-dinitrophenylhydrazine, and therefore is probably indole-3-aldehyde. Additional routes of tryptophan degradation have been found in microorganisms, and are summarized briefly in Figure 15. It is not yet known whether these pathways are utilized by other plants. The most interesting pathway is the conversion of tryptophan to nicotinic acid, and it would not at all be surprising if this transformation were of widespread occurrence in the plant kingdom.

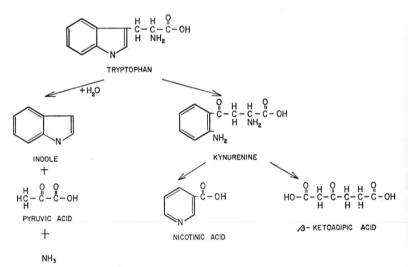

Figure 15. Pathways of tryptophan degradation.

*Phenylalanine and tyrosine.* Probably the outstanding example of the clarification of a difficult pathway of biosynthesis is found in the elucidation by Davis of the manner in which phenylalanine and tyrosine are synthesized. Our knowledge of this metabolic sequence is again due chiefly to a combination of studies with mutant strains of microorganisms and with isotopic precursors. The identification of substances accumulated by bacterial mutants blocked in different stages of synthesis has led to the formulation (Davis, 1955a,b,c) of the reaction sequence presented in Figure 16. The important intermediate here is shikimic acid, a substance that occurs in many plants. The precursor of shikimic acid, 5-dehydroshikimic acid, serves as a growth factor for mutants having still earlier blocks in the biosynthetic pathway. The enzyme which

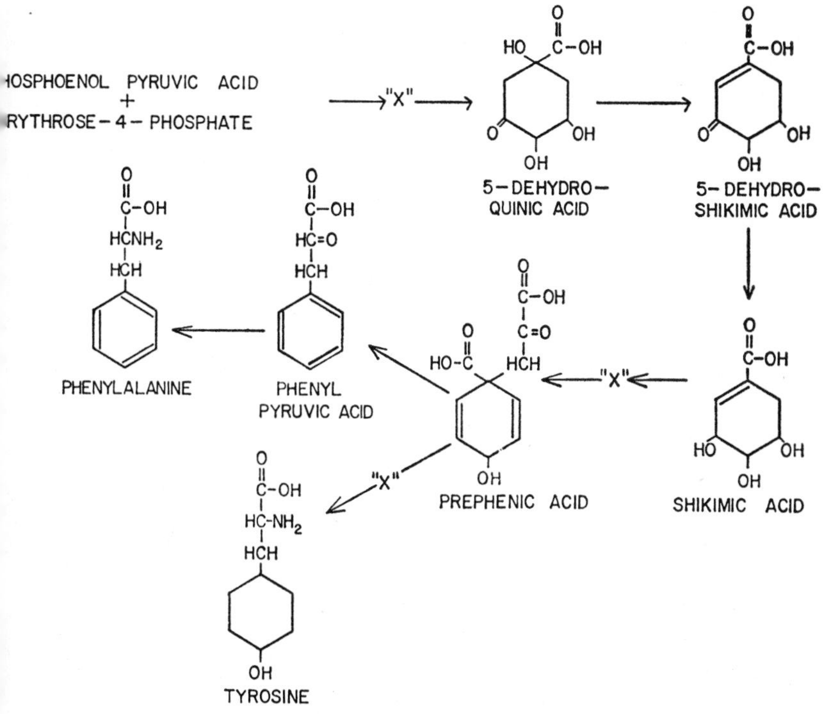

Figure 16. Biosynthesis of phenylalanine and tyrosine.

reduces dehydroshikimic acid to shikimic acid has been isolated, and requires TPNH as a cofactor. The enzyme is not present in a mutant which is blocked between dehydroshikimic and shikimic acids. The enzyme which converts 5-dehydroquinic to 5-dehydroshikimic acid likewise has been isolated. Here again, mutants in which the conversion of dehydroquinic to dehydroshikimic acid is blocked do not possess this enzyme.

The steps leading to the formation of dehydroquinic acid have been clarified by the use of isotopes. Preliminary investigations with glucose labeled in specific carbons (Davis, 1955b; Sprinson, 1955) indicated that carbons 1 and 2 plus the carboxyl carbon (Figure 16) are derived from a 3-carbon glycolytic intermediate, while carbons 3,4,5, and 6 arise from the pentose-sedoheptulose pathway. This has led to the recognition of phosphoenolpyruvate and D-erythrose-4-phosphate as the simple precursors of dehydroquinic acid (Srinivasan, et al., 1955). Reference to Figure 16 will show that the steps between shikimic and prephenic acids are not yet clear, but the availability of both mutants and isotopically labeled compounds should result in a clarification of these steps in the near future.

*Metabolism of non-protein amino acids.* Although little is known as yet concerning the metabolism of many of the amino acids described in Table IV, their unusual nature makes both their function and their metabolism of considerable interest. The finding of γ-methyleneglutamine, γ-methyleneglutamate, γ-methylene-α-ketoglutarate, γ-methylglutamate, γ-methyl-γ-hydroxyglutamate, and γ-methyl-γ-hydroxy-α-ketoglutarate in plants suggests a metabolic relationship between these compounds. Grobbelaar, et al. (1955) have suggested that γ-methyl-γ-hydroxy-α-ketoglutarate could be formed by the condensation of two molecules of pyruvate, a reaction employed in the chemical synthesis of the compound. The other α-keto acids could then be formed from γ-methyl-γ-hydroxy-α-ketoglutarate by the reactions outlined in Figure 17. From each of these α-keto acids, the corresponding amino acids could be formed by transamination, while γ-methyleneglutamine could arise from γ-methyleneglutamate in the same manner that glutamine is formed from glutamate (Chapter 3). The enzymatic formation of γ-methyleneglutamate from γ-methylene-α-ketoglutarate and γ-methylglutamate from γ-methyl-α-ketoglutarate, by transamination with glutamate has already been demonstrated by Fowden and Done (1953). It has also been observed that γ-methyleneglutamate is decarboxylated by various plant extracts (Fowden, 1954). In view of these results, it would be of considerable interest to determine whether the pathways in Figure 17 actually exist. Examination of Table IV indicates that there are many important and interesting studies (especially with tracers) to be performed on the metabolism of these many different amino acids.

*Photosynthetic and non-photosynthetic incorporation of metabolites into amino acids.* Racusen and Aronoff (1954) have investigated the incorporation of $C^{14}O_2$ into the amino acids of excised soybean leaves in the dark. After sixty minutes, analysis showed the greatest radioactivity in arginine, followed by glutamate, aspartate, asparagine, serine, glycine, and alanine. The results are similar to those obtained by Abelson (1952) with bacteria. In arginine, 75% of the radioactivity occurs in the guanido carbon, which Racusen and Aronoff interpret as resulting from the operation of an ornithine cycle in the leaves. The data concerning the incorporation of $C^{14}O_2$ into the other amino acids are consistent with known carboxylation reactions, and with the pathways of amino acid synthesis already presented in this discussion.

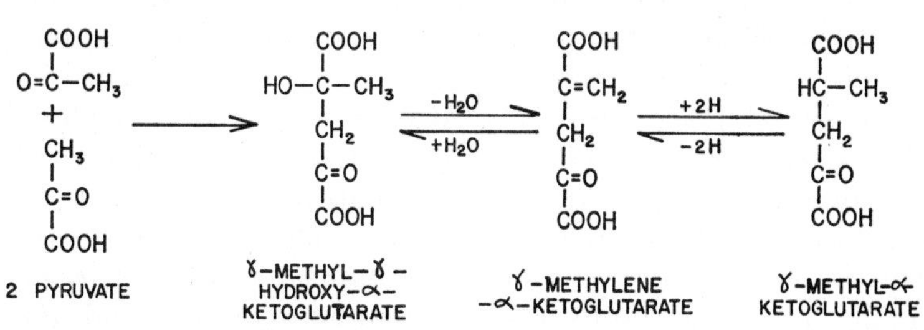

Figure 17. Suggested pathways of metabolism of methylated $\alpha$-ketoglutarate compounds.

Observations that are also consistent with the operation of the Krebs cycle and the pathways outlined above have been made by Rogers (1955b). He has found that excised leaves and roots of bean plants incorporate the carbons of both sucrose and acetate into amino acids. The carbons of sucrose are transformed most rapidly into alanine, glutamate, and aspartate, followed by glycine, threonine, phenylalanine, valine, and methionine. Acetate carbons are likewise incorporated most rapidly into glutamate and aspartate, and more slowly into other amino acids. Interestingly, acetate carbons are only slowly incorporated into leucine and valine by bean plants. This is in contrast to guayule where Arreguin, *et al.* (1951) found acetate carbons incorporated into these amino acids in greater amounts than into any other substance.

Photosynthetic incorporation of $C^{14}O_2$ into amino acids principally reflects the different rates at which various carbon skeletons become available during photosynthetic as compared with non-photosynthetic conditions. This is particularly evident during the early stages of photosynthesis. Thus, after thirty seconds of photosynthesis in $C^{14}O_2$, not only phosphoglycerate and malate, but also alanine and aspartate are labeled (Stepka, *et al.*, 1948). After ninety seconds in $C^{14}O_2$, glycine and serine also become labeled (Vernon and Aronoff, 1950). This labeling pattern is probably due to the transformation of phosphoglycerate to alanine (via pyruvate), malate to aspartate (via oxalacetate), ribulose-5-phosphate to glycine (Weissbach and Horecker, 1955), and glycine to serine. After one hour of photosynthesis, high activity occurs in alanine, glycine, serine, aspartate, and glutamate, and lesser activity in phenylalanine, tyrosine, proline, leucine, and arginine (Racusen and Aronoff, 1954). After longer periods of photosynthesis, all amino acids are labeled, and the pattern of labeling becomes progressively so similar to that obtained in the dark or in non-photosynthetic tissues that essentially all distinction due to the effect of light disappears (Schieler, *et al.*, 1953). Thus, the results obtained by photosynthetic and non-photosynthetic $CO_2$ incorporation into amino acids seem clearly compatible. An even more important appraisal of the above results, however, is their consistency with known pathways of both carbohydrate and amino acid metabolism.

*Summary*. From this brief discussion it is obvious that our knowledge of the chemical pathways involved in the synthesis and breakdown of amino acids is slowly becoming clearer. However, the tremendous progress in the past few years should not blind us to the many gaps that still remain, and to the many opportunities for exciting research that these gaps provide. In addition, it is important that further information be obtained as to whether the metabolic pathways that have been clarified so brilliantly with *Neurospora* or *E. coli* are of general occurrence in plants. Our limited knowledge on this point supports the thesis that these pathways do indeed occur generally, but nothing is so convincing as concrete evidence.

## REFERENCES

ABELSON, P. H., Jour. Biol. Chem. **206,** 335 (1954).

ABELSON, P. H. AND VOGEL, H. J., Jour. Biol. Chem. **213,** 355 (1955).

ABELSON, P. H., BOLTON, E. T., AND ALDOUS, E., Jour. Biol. Chem. **198,** 165 (1952).

ADAMS, E., Jour. Biol. Chem. **209,** 829 (1954).

ADELBERG, E. A., in *Amino Acid Metabolism* (McElroy, W. D. and Glass, B., Eds.), Johns Hopkins Press, Baltimore (1955).

ALBAUM, H. AND COHEN, P. P., Jour. Biol. Chem. **149,** 19 (1943).

ALSOPP, A., Nature **161,** 833 (1948).

AMES, B., in *Amino Acid Metabolism* (McElroy, W. D. and Glass, B., Eds.), Johns Hopkins Press, Baltimore (1955).

AMES, B. AND MITCHELL, H. K., Jour. Biol. Chem. **212,** 687 (1955).

AMES, B., MITCHELL, H. K., AND MITCHELL, M. B., Jour. Am. Chem. Soc. **75,** 1015 (1953).

ARREGUIN, B., BONNER, J., AND WOOD, B. J., Arch. Biochem. Biophys. **31,** 234 (1951).

BEEVERS, H., Biochem. Jour. **48,** 132 (1951).

BENDER, A. E. AND KREBS, H. A., Biochem. Jour. **46,** 210 (1950).

BENSON, A. A. AND CALVIN, M., Jour. Exp. Botany **1,** 63 (1950).

BERG, A. M., KARI, S., ALFTHAN, M., AND VIRTANEN, A. I., Acta Chem. Scand. **8,** 358 (1954).

BLACK, S. AND GRAY, N., Jour. Am. Chem. Soc. **75,** 2271 (1953).

BLACK, S. AND WRIGHT, N. G., Jour. Biol. Chem. **213,** 51 (1955a).

BLACK, S. AND WRIGHT, N. G., in *Amino Acid Metabolism* (McElroy, W. D. and Glass, B., Eds.), Johns Hopkins Press, Baltimore (1955b).

BORSOOK, H., ABRAMS, A., AND LOWY, P. H., Jour. Biol. Chem. **215,** 111 (1955).

BRAUNSTEIN, A. E. AND KRITZMANN, M. G., Enzymologia **2,** 129 (1937).

COHEN, P. P., Biochem. Jour. **33,** 1478 (1939).

COON, M. J., Federation Proc. **14,** 762 (1955a).

COON, M. J., ROBINSON, W. G., AND BACHHAWAT, B. K., in *Amino Acid Metabo-*

*lism* (McElroy, W. D. and Glass, B., Eds.), Johns Hopkins Press, Baltimore (1955b).

DAVIS, B. D., Experientia **6,** 41 (1950).

DAVIS, B. D., Nature **169,** 534 (1952).

DAVIS, B. D., Adv. in Enzymol. **16,** 247 (1955a).

DAVIS, B. D., Federation Proc. 14, 691 (1955b).

DAVIS, B. D., in *Amino Acid Metabolism* (McElroy, W. D. and Glass, B., Eds.), Johns Hopkins Press, Baltimore (1955c).

DAVISON, D. C. AND ELLIOTT, W. H., Nature **169,** 313 (1952).

DENT, C. E., Biochem. Jour. **43,** 169 (1948).

DENT, C. E., STEPKA, W., AND STEWARD, F. C., Nature **160,** 682 (1947).

DEWEY, D. L. AND WORK, E., Nature **169,** 533 (1952).

DONE, J. AND FOWDEN, L., Biochem. Jour. **51,** 451 (1952).

FINCHAM, J. R. S., Biochem. Jour. **53,** 313 (1953).

FOWDEN, L., Jour. Exp. Botany **5,** 28 (1954).

FOWDEN, L., Nature **176,** 347 (1955).

FOWDEN, L. AND DONE, G., Nature **171,** 1068 (1953).

GORDON, S. AND NIEVA, F., Arch. Biochem. Biophys. **20,** 356 (1948).

GREENBERG, J. B., GALSTON, A. W., SHAW, K. N. F., AND ARMSTRONG, M. D., Science **125,** 992 (1957).

GROBBELAAR, N. AND STEWARD, F. C., Jour. Am. Chem. Soc. **75,** 4341 (1953).

GROBBELAAR, N., POLLARD, J. K., AND STEWARD, F. C., Nature **175,** 703 (1955).

GUGGENHEIM, M., Zeit. Physiol. Chem. **88,** 276 (1913).

HAAS, F., MITCHELL, M. B., AMES, B., AND MITCHELL, H. K., Genetics **37,** 217 (1952).

HERBST, R. M. AND ENGEL, L. L., Jour. Biol. Chem. **107,** 505 (1934).

HOOD, S. L., Botan. Gaz. **116,** 86 (1954).

HULME, A. C. AND ARTHINGTON, W., Nature **165,** 716 (1950).

HULME, A. C. AND ARTHINGTON, W., Nature **173,** 588 (1954).

HULME, A. C. AND STEWARD, F. C., Nature **175,** 171 (1955).

JAHN, K., Arch. Pharm. **229,** 669 (1891).

JOHNSTON, J. A., RACUSEN, D., AND BONNER, J., Proc. Natl. Acad. Sci. **40,** 1031 (1954).

JONES, M. E., SPECTOR, L., AND LIPMANN, F., Jour. Am. Chem. Soc. **77,** 819 (1955).

KASTING, R. AND DELWICHE, C., Plant Physiol. **30,** (Suppl.), 28 (1955).

KING, F. E., KING, T. J., AND WARWICK, A. J., Jour. Chem. Soc. 3590 (1950).

KISLIUK, R. AND SAKAMI, W., Jour. Am. Chem. Soc. **76,** 1456 (1954).

KITAGAWA, M. AND MONOBE, S., Jour. Biochem. (Japan) **18,** 333 (1933).

KNIVETT, V. A., Biochem. Jour. **56,** 602 (1954).

KORZENOVSKY, M. AND WERKMAN, C. H., Arch. Biochem. Biophys. **46,** 174 (1953).

KRITZMANN, M. G., Nature **143,** 603 (1939).

LEONARD, M. J. K. AND BURRIS, R. H., Jour. Biol. Chem. **170,** 701 (1947).

LEVY, L. AND COON, M. J., Jour. Biol. Chem. **192,** 807 (1951).

LEVY, L. AND COON, M. J., Federation Proc. **11,** 248 (1952).

LOWY, P. H., Arch. Biochem. Biophys. **47,** 228 (1952).

LUGG, J. W. H., Adv. in Protein Chem. **5,** 229 (1949).

MASCRE, M., Compt. rend. **204,** 890 (1937).

McCALLA, A. G., Ann. Rev. Biochem. **18,** 615, (1949).

MEISTER, A., Federation Proc. **14,** 683 (1955).

METZLER, D. AND SNELL, E. E., Jour. Am. Chem. Soc. **74,** 979 (1952).

MIETTINEN, J. K. AND VIRTANEN, A. I., Acta Chem. Scand. **7,** 289 (1953a).

MIETTINEN, J. K. AND VIRTANEN, A. I., Acta Chem. Scand. 7, 1243 (1953b).

MIETTINEN, J. K., KARI, S., MOISIO, T., ALFTHAN, M., AND VIRTANEN, A. I., Suomen Kemistilehti B26, 26 (1953).

MITCHELL, H. K. AND HOULAHAN, M. B., Jour. Biol. Chem. 174, 883 (1948).

MORRIS, C. J. AND THOMPSON, J. F., Jour. Am. Chem. Soc. 78, 1605 (1956).

NISMAN, B., COHEN, G., WIESENDANGER, S., AND HIRSCH, M., Compt. rend. 238, 1342 (1954).

RACUSEN, D. W., The Incorporation of Carbon-14 into Leaf Amino Acids and Protein. Doctoral Dissertation, Iowa State College, 1953.

RACUSEN, D. AND ARONOFF, S., Arch. Biochem. Biophys. 51, 68 (1954).

RADHAKRISHNAN, A. N. AND GIRI, K. V., Biochem. Jour. 58, 57 (1954).

RATNER, S., PETRACK, B., AND ROCHOVANSKY, O., Jour. Biol. Chem. 204, 95 (1953).

ROEPKE, R. R., LIBBY, R. L., AND SMALL, M. H., Jour. Bact. 48, 409 (1944).

ROGERS, B. J., Plant Physiol. 30, 186 (1955a).

ROGERS, B. J., Plant Physiol. 30, 377 (1955b).

ROTHSTEIN, M. AND MILLER, L. L., Jour. Biol. Chem. 206, 243 (1954).

SAKATO, Y., Jour. Ag. Chem. Soc. Japan 23, 262 (1950).

SCHALES, O., MIMS, V., AND SCHALES, S., Arch. Biochem. 10, 455 (1946).

SCHIELER, L., McCLURE, L. E., AND DUNN, M. S., Jour. Biol. Chem. 203, 1039 (1953).

SCHWEET, R., HOLDEN, J., AND LOWY, P. H., Jour. Biol. Chem. 211, 517 (1954).

SPRINSON, D. B., in Amino Acid Metabolism (McElroy, W. D. and Glass, B., Eds.), Johns Hopkins Press, Baltimore (1955).

SRB, A. AND HOROWITZ, N., Jour. Biol. Chem. 154, 129 (1944).

SRINIVASAN, P. R., KATAGIRI, M., AND SPRINSON, D. B., Jour. Am. Chem. Soc. 77, 4943 (1955).

STEPKA, W., BENSON, A. A., AND CALVIN, M., Science 108, 304 (1948).

STETTEN, M. R. AND SCHOENHEIMER, R., Jour. Biol. Chem. 153, 113 (1944).

STEWARD, F. C. AND THOMPSON, J. F., Ann. Rev. Plant Physiol. 1, 233 (1950).

STEWARD, F. C., WETMORE, R. H., AND POLLARD, J. K., Am. Jour. Botany 42, 946 (1955).

STEWARD, F. C., WETMORE, R. H., THOMPSON, J. F., AND NITSCH, J. P., Am. Jour. Botany 41, 123 (1954).

STOLL, A. AND SEEBECK, E., Experientia 3, 114 (1947).

STRASSMAN, M., LOCKE, L. A., THOMAS, A. J., AND WEINHOUSE, S., Jour. Am. Chem. Soc. 78, 1599 (1956).

STUMPF, P. K., Federation Proc. 10, 256 (1951).

SYNGE, R. L. M. AND WOOD, J. C., Biochem. Jour. 64, 252 (1956).

TANG, Y. W. AND BONNER, J., Arch. Biochem. 13, 11 (1947).

TEAS, H., HOROWITZ, N., AND FLING, M., Jour. Biol. Chem. 172, 651 (1948).

THAYER, P. AND HOROWITZ, N., Jour. Biol. Chem. 192, 755 (1951).

THIMANN, K. V., Jour. Biol. Chem. 109, 279 (1952).

THOMPSON, J. F., MORRIS, C. J., AND ZACHARIUS, R. M., Nature 178, 593 (1956).

TOLBERT, N. E., Jour. Biol. Chem. 215, 27 (1955).

TOLBERT, N. E. AND COHAN, M. S., Jour. Biol. Chem. 204, 649 (1954).

TOLBERT, N. E., CLAGETT, C. O., AND BURRIS, R. H., Jour. Biol. Chem. 181, 905 (1949).

TRISTRAM, G. R., in The Proteins (Neurath, H. and Bailey, K., Eds.) 1, 181 (1953).

UMBREIT, W., WOOD, W., AND GUNSALUS, I. C., Jour. Biol. Chem. 165, 731 (1946).

URBACH, G. E., Nature 175, 170 (1955).

VAN VEEN, A. G. AND HYMAN, A. J., Rec. Trav. Chim. 54, 493 (1935).

VERNON, L. P. AND ARONOFF, S., Arch. Biochem. 29, 179 (1950).

VIRTANEN, A. I., Angewandte Chemie 67, 381 (1955).

VIRTANEN, A. I. AND BERG, A. M., Acta Chem. Scand. 8, 1085 (1954).

VIRTANEN, A. I. AND BERG, A. M., Acta Chem. Scand. 9, 553 (1955).

VIRTANEN, A. I. AND HIETALA, P. K., Acta Chem. Scand. 9, 175 (1955).

VIRTANEN, A. I. AND KARI, S., Acta Chem. Scand. 8, 1290 (1954).

VIRTANEN, A. I. AND KARI, S., Acta Chem. Scand. 9, 170 (1955).

VIRTANEN, A. I. AND LAINE, T., Nature 141, 748 (1938).

VIRTANEN, A. I. AND LINKO, P., Acta Chem. Scand. 9, 531 (1955).

VIRTANEN, A. I. AND MIETTINEN, J. K., Biochim. Biophys. Acta 12, 181 (1953).

VIRTANEN, A. I., UKSILA, E., AND MATIKKALA, E. J., Acta Chem. Scand. 8, 1091 (1954).

VOGEL, H. J., Proc. Natl. Acad. Sci. 39, 578 (1953).

VOGEL, H. J. AND BONNER, D. M., Proc. Natl. Acad. Sci. 40, 688 (1954).

VOGEL, H. J. AND DAVIS, B. D., Jour. Am. Chem. Soc. 74, 109 (1952).

VOGEL, H. J., ABELSON, P. H., AND BOLTON, E. T., Biochim. Biophys. Acta 11, 584 (1953).

WADA, M., Proc. Imp. Acad. (Japan) 6, 15 (1930).

WAGENKNECHT, A. C. AND BURRIS, R. H., Arch. Biochem. 25, 30 (1949).

WALKER, J. B., Proc. Natl. Acad. Sci. 38, 561 (1952).

WALKER, J. B. AND MYERS, J., Jour. Biol. Chem. 203, 143 (1953).

WATANABE, Y. AND SHIMURA, K., Jour. Biochem. (Japan) 43, 283 (1956).

WEBSTER, G. C. AND VARNER, J. E., Jour. Biol. Chem. 215, 91 (1955).

WEINSTOCK, H., MITCHELL, H. K., PRATT, E., AND WILLIAMS, R. J., Jour. Am. Chem. Soc. 61, 1421 (1939).

WEISSBACH, A. AND HORECKER, B. L., in *Amino Acid Metabolism* (McElroy, W. D. and Glass, B., Eds.), Johns Hopkins Press, Baltimore (1955).

WHITE, E., New Zealand Jour. Sci. Technol. 25B, 137 (1944).

WILDMAN, S., FERRI, M., AND BONNER, J., Arch. Biochem. 13, 131 (1947).

WILSON, D. G., KING, K. W., AND BURRIS, R. H., Jour. Biol. Chem. 208, 863 (1954).

WINDSOR, E., Jour. Biol. Chem. 192, 595 (1951a).

WINDSOR, E., Jour. Biol. Chem. 192, 607 (1951b).

WOHL, A. AND JOHNSON, A., Ber. Deut. Chem. Ges. 40, 4712 (1907).

YANOFSKY, C., Jour. Biol. Chem. 194, 279 (1952).

YOSHIDA, T. AND FUKUYAMA, S., Jour. Biochem. (Japan) 34, 429 (1941).

ZACCHARIUS, R. M., THOMPSON, J. F., AND STEWARD, F. C., Jour. Am. Chem. Soc. 74, 2949 (1952).

ZELITCH, I., Federation Proc. 16, 276 (1957).

# Chapter 3

# Biosynthesis of
# Amides and Peptides

The occurrence of the amides, glutamine and asparagine, in plants is well established. In recent years, an increasing number of peptides and peptide-like substances have also been found in plants (Bricas and Fromageot, 1953; Meister, 1957). These include true peptides, vitamins and their conjugates, antibiotic substances, and certain materials toxic to animals. A partial listing of these compounds is given in Table VI. Probably the discovery of such interesting substances is only beginning. The function of most of the peptides, except the vitamins and glutathione, is still unknown.

Our knowledge of the metabolism, and especially the biosynthesis, of amides and peptides is a product of relatively recent investigations and concepts. Of great importance is the concept of the key position of adenosine triphosphate (ATP) in biological syntheses. As will be seen from the following discussion, recognition of the necessity of ATP for peptide and amide syntheses has been the factor responsible for much new information on the biochemistry of nitrogen metabolism.

*Biosynthesis of glutamine.* For many years, plant scientists recognized that glutamine is an important participant in the nitrogen metabolism of plants (Chibnall, 1939). The manner in which glutamine synthesis proceeds was completely obscure, however. Glutamine is hydrolyzed by the enzyme glutaminase:

$$\text{glutamine} + H_2O \rightarrow \text{glutamate} + NH_3 \qquad (a)$$

but the equilibrium for this reaction is so far in the direction of glutamate and ammonia that any significant synthesis by a simple reversal of the hydrolytic process is improbable.

The first real insight into the manner of glutamine syn-

## TABLE VI

### Some Peptides and Related Substances in Plants

| Peptide | Composition | Source |
|---|---|---|
| Glutathione | γ-glutamylcysteinylglycine | Corn, potato, yeast (Hopkins, 1921; Schroeder and Woodward, 1939). |
| γ-Glutamylalanine | — | Pea seedlings (Virtanen and Berg, 1954). |
| Pantothenic acid | pantoyl-β-alanine | Most plants |
| Folic acid | pteroylglutamic acid | Spinach (Mitchell, et al., 1944). |
| Folic acid conjugate | pteroylheptaglutamic acid | Yeast (Pfiffner, et al., 1945). |
| Peptide of p-amino-benzoic acid | 1 p-aminobenzoic acid + 10 glutamic acid + 1 unidentified α-amino acid + 1 ammonia residue | Yeast (Ratner, et al., 1944). |
| Biocytin | biotinyl lysine | Yeast (Wolf, et al., 1952). |
| Lycomarasmin | asparagine, glycine, and some derivative of pyruvate | Fusarium lycopersici (Plattner and Clauson-Kass, 1945). |
| Ergot peptides | lysergic acid, proline, and phenylalanine, leucine or valine | Rye ergot (Claviceps purpurea) (Tanret, 1875; Stoll, et al., 1951). |
| Phalloidin | cysteine, alanine, allohydroxyproline, and α-hydroxytryptophan | Amanita Phalloides (Wieland and Witkop, 1940). |
| Pyrrollodonyl-α-glutaminyl-glutamine | — | Pelvetia fastigiata (Dekker, et al., 1949). |
| Viscotoxin | cysteine, serine, arginine, glucuronic acid and a substituted naphthalene ring | Viscum album (mistletoe) (Winterfeld and Rink, 1948). |
| β-(N-γ-L-Glutamyl)-Amino-propionitrile | — | Lathyrus odoratus seeds (Schilling and Strong, 1955). |

thesis in plants was obtained by Elliott (1951) with cell-free extracts of lupine seedlings. He found that such extracts could catalyze the synthesis of γ-glutamyl hydroxamate from glutamate and hydroxylamine, if ATP and magnesium ions were present. A number of plant extracts were subsequently shown to catalyze glutamyl hydroxamate synthesis in the same manner (Webster, 1953). If ammonia is substituted for hydroxylamine, the plant extracts catalyze a net synthesis of glutamine. The complete reactions have been demonstrated to be (Elliott, 1953; Webster, 1953):

$$\text{glutamate} + \text{NH}_3 + \text{ATP} \xrightleftharpoons{\text{Mg}^{++}} \text{glutamine} + \text{ADP} + \text{P}_i. \quad \text{(b)}$$

$$\text{glutamate} + \text{NH}_2\text{OH} + \text{ATP} \xrightarrow{\text{Mg}^{++}}$$
$$\text{glutamyl hydroxamate} + \text{ADP} + \text{P}_i. \quad \text{(c)}$$

The enzyme, glutamine synthetase, catalyzes both reactions, as well as the synthesis of glutamyl hydrazide if hydrazine is substituted for ammonia. Glutamine synthetase has been purified several thousand-fold from extracts of pea seeds, and subjected to extensive characterization (Elliott, 1953; Varner and Webster, 1955; Levintow, et al., 1955). The synthesis of glutamine by reaction (b) is reversible to a measurable extent, and thus can result in a net synthesis of ATP at the expense of glutamine. From the equilibrium constant of reaction (b), it has been calculated that there is a difference of about −4300 calories between the standard free energy of hydrolysis of glutamine and of ATP (Levintow and Meister, 1954; Varner and Webster, 1955).

In addition to catalyzing glutamine synthesis, glutamine synthetase catalyzes the following reactions:

$$\text{glutamine} + \text{N}^{15}\text{H}_3 \xrightarrow{\text{Mg}^{++}, \text{ADP}, \text{P}_i} \text{glutamine-N}^{15} + \text{NH}_3 \quad \text{(d)}$$

$$\text{glutamine} + \text{NH}_2\text{OH} \xrightarrow{\text{Mg}^{++}, \text{ADP}, \text{P}_i}$$
$$\text{glutamyl hydroxamate} + \text{NH}_3 \quad \text{(e)}$$

$$\text{glutamine} + \text{H}_2\text{O} \xrightarrow{\text{Mg}^{++}, \text{ADP}, \text{As}_i} \text{glutamate} + \text{NH}_3 \quad \text{(f)}$$

Reactions (d) and (e) are glutamyl transfer reactions, first observed by Stumpf and Loomis (1950) in pumpkin seedling

extracts. They are actually transfers of the glutamyl moiety
of glutamine from ammonia to $N^{15}$-ammonia or to hydroxylamine. However, they require a bewildering set of cofactors: ADP, magnesium or manganese ions, and phosphate
or arsenate. Although both manganese and arsenate are very
poor cofactors for the glutamine synthesis reaction, they are
considerably more effective than magnesium and phosphate
ions for the transfer reaction. Finally, reaction (f) is essentially an arsenate-promoted hydrolysis (or arsenolysis) of
glutamine, and has the same cofactor requirements as the
glutamyl transfer reactions.

The exact mechanism by which ATP is able to participate
in glutamine synthesis is of considerable interest because
it may be considered a model for the participation of ATP
in a number of biosynthetic processes. Early indirect studies
(Elliott, 1953; Webster, 1953) cast doubt on the formation
of free glutamyl phosphate or glutamyl-coenzyme A as intermediates in glutamine synthesis. Further investigation by
Levintow and Meister (1956) has likewise demonstrated that
synthetic glutamyl phosphate is not converted to glutamine
by glutamine synthetase. The studies of Boyer, *et al.* (1956)
and Kowalsky, *et al.* (1956), however, have shown that the
carboxyl oxygen of glutamate is incorporated into the liberated orthophosphate during glutamine synthesis.

$$HOOC—CHNH_2(CH_2)_2COO^{18}H + NH_3 + ATP \rightleftharpoons$$

$$HOOC—CHNH_2(CH_2)_2CONH_2 + ADP + HO^{18}—PO(OH)_2$$

This provides strong evidence for the intermediate formation
of a linkage between glutamate and phosphate during glutamine synthesis. These apparent differences can be resolved
partly by the assumption that glutamine synthesis involves
the formation of an enzyme-bound glutamyl phosphate.

Such a mechanism is consistent with many of the other activities of glutamine synthetase. For example, the glutamyl transfer reaction would then proceed as follows:

$$E + ADP + P_i + Glutamine \rightleftharpoons E \diagdown^{Glutamyl-P}_{ADP} + NH_3$$

$$E \diagdown^{Glutamyl-P}_{ADP} + N^{15}H_3 \rightleftharpoons E + Glutamine-N^{15} + ADP + P_i$$

This formulation does not provide a ready explanation of the greater effectiveness of arsenate over phosphate in glutamyl transfer, but this is principally a reflection of our ignorance of the actual mechanism involved in the effect of arsenate on many biochemical reactions. If one assumes that the carboxyl-arsenate bond is more reactive than the carboxyl-phosphate bond, then the greater effectiveness of arsenate is obvious. This would also explain the arsenate-activated hydrolysis of glutamine catalyzed by glutamine synthetase, as glutamyl-arsenate would react more readily with water.

$$E + ADP + Glutamine + As_i \rightarrow E \diagdown^{Glutamyl-As}_{ADP} \rightarrow$$

$$E + Glutamate + As_i + ADP + NH_3$$

Evidence that a glutamyl-arsenate intermediate is formed during the arsenolysis of glutamine has been obtained by Varner, *et al.* (1958), who showed that the oxygen of arsenate labeled with oxygen-18 is transferred to the carboxyl of the glutamate formed as a result of arsenolysis.

The mechanism outlined above does not account for the apparent requirement for ADP for either the transfer or arsenolysis reactions. One possibility is that ADP, which is essential for the reversal of glutamine synthesis, must be in place on the enzyme surface before phosphate can replace the amide group of glutamine. A possible sequence of events during the formation of enzyme-bound glutamyl-phosphate is:

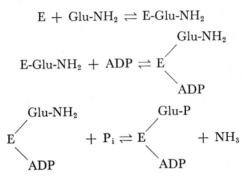

$$E + Glu\text{-}NH_2 \rightleftharpoons E\text{-}Glu\text{-}NH_2$$

$$E\text{-}Glu\text{-}NH_2 + ADP \rightleftharpoons E\diagdown^{Glu\text{-}NH_2}_{ADP}$$

$$E\diagdown^{Glu\text{-}NH_2}_{ADP} + P_i \rightleftharpoons E\diagdown^{Glu\text{-}P}_{ADP} + NH_3$$

By the use of stoichiometric quantities of enzyme, and labeled substrates, the existence of a sequence such as this might be tested.

It can be seen that the synthesis of glutamine presents a complex and difficult problem. Further studies on the mechanism of glutamine synthesis, however, should reveal much concerning the intimate details of the manner in which ATP is utilized in biological syntheses.

All pertinent observations with intact cells are consistent with the view that cellular glutamine synthesis is catalyzed by glutamine synthetase. Most important are the observations that glutamate is directly converted to glutamine, *in vivo* (Webster, 1954; Nelson and Krotkov, 1956), and that respiratory or photosynthetic energy is necessary for cellular glutamine synthesis (Naylor and Tolbert, 1955). It would be of interest to determine, if possible, whether the carboxyl oxygen of glutamate-$O^{18}$ is transferred *in the cell* to orthophosphate, as it is with the isolated enzyme. If such a transfer occurs, it would provide compelling evidence for the participation of glutamine synthetase in cellular glutamine synthesis.

Although glutamine is often regarded principally as a means for the reversible storage in plants of ammonia in non-toxic form, evidence is accumulating which indicates the importance of glutamine in many phases of metabolism. Thus, a considerable portion of protein glutamate is often glutamine, and recent studies with mammalian systems have shown that glutamine, not glutamate, is the precursor of protein glutamine. Glutamine also is a specific nitrogen donor for nitrogen atoms 3 and 9 in the purine ring (Sonne, et al., 1953), and is specifically required in at least some organisms for the biosynthesis of guanosine-5'-phosphate from xanthosine-5'-phosphate (Bentley and Abrams, 1956). Glutamine is also required for the conversion of hexose-6-phosphate to glucosamine-6-phosphate by *Neurospora* (Leloir and Cardini, 1953). Finally, the demonstrated reversibility of the glutamine synthetase reaction raises a question of whether the breakdown of stored glutamine might be not only a source of glutamate and ammonia, but also a source of ATP. Such a source, under conditions of extensive glutamine disappearance in a plant, could be of definite significance.

*Biosynthesis of asparagine.* Despite the fact that asparagine constitutes the principal form of nitrogen in many plants, our knowledge of asparagine synthesis is considerably less than our knowledge of glutamine synthesis. This has given rise to much unfounded speculation, such as the repeated suggestion that asparagine arises only by the release of asparagine from the degradation of protein. Aside from not explaining how protein asparagine is formed in the first place, this suggestion is rendered untenable by the fact that the amount of asparagine formed by a germinating seedling (lupine, for example) is many times greater than the asparagine content of the total protein of the seedling.

The first serious study of the actual mechanism of asparagine synthesis was made by Elliott (1951). He tested the possibility that aspartyl hydroxamate might be formed by a direct condensation of aspartate and hydroxylamine in the presence of ATP. However, when he incubated cell-free extracts of lupine seedlings with aspartate, hydroxylamine, ATP, and magnesium ions, no detectable formation of aspartyl hydroxamate occurred. As this same cell-free extract readily formed glutamyl hydroxamate (by the action of glutamine synthetase) when aspartate was replaced by glutamate, the results raised a question as to whether asparagine synthesis proceeds in the same manner as glutamine synthesis. A number of alternate possibilities for asparagine synthesis were, therefore, examined. Mardashev and Lestrovoya (1951) reported that liver extracts catalyze an amide transfer from glutamine to aspartate. Examination of this possibility in plant extracts in the presence of $C^{14}$-aspartate revealed no formation of $C^{14}$-asparagine (Webster and Varner, 1955). Meister and Fraser (1954) demonstrated that liver extracts catalyze asparagine synthesis by transamination between some α-amino acid and α-ketosuccinamate. However, the synthesis of α-ketosuccinamate has not been demonstrated, except from asparagine, so the significance of the reaction is not clear.

A third possibility for asparagine synthesis is the biosynthesis of β-alanylamide and its carboxylation to asparagine. This possibility was tested by Webster and Varner (1955), who measured the carboxylation of β-alanylamide to asparagine with $C^{14}O_2$. Table VII presents some of the results obtained, and indicates: (a) that β-alanylamide is probably hydrolyzed to β-alanine before carboxylation to aspartate and subsequent conversion to asparagine, and (b) aspartate is converted into asparagine. This finding raises the question that asparagine may indeed be synthesized directly from aspartate, even though aspartyl hydroxamate is not. Such a conclusion is also derived from various labeling experiments with intact cells. For example, Nelson and Krotkov (1956) exposed broad-bean leaves to $C^{14}O_2$ and determined the distribution of labeling in glutamate, glutamine, aspartate, and

TABLE VII

Carboxylation Reactions Involving β-Alanine and
β-Alanylamide in Wheat Germ Extracts[1]

| System | cts/min. in aspartate | cts/min. in asparagine |
|---|---|---|
| β-alanine + $C^{14}O_2$ | 45,380 | 3063 |
| β-alanylamide + $C^{14}O_2$ | 5,160 | 951 |

[1] Adapted from Webster and Varner (1955).

asparagine. Not only was the distribution the same in glutamine as it was in glutamate, but also the distribution of label
in asparagine was the same as that in aspartate. Nelson and
Krotkov concluded that glutamine is formed from glutamate
and asparagine is formed from aspartate. Webster and Varner
(1955) found that, under certain conditions, intact lupine
seedlings incorporate the carbons of $C^{14}$-aspartate into asparagine. Under such circumstances, if uniformly labeled aspartate is employed, uniformly labeled asparagine is obtained.
If aspartate labeled in carbon atom number-4 is used, asparagine labeled in carbon atom number-4 is obtained. Yamomoto
(1955) has observed that *Vigna sesquipedalis* hypocotyls, when
incubated for three hours with aspartate and ammonia, exhibit a four-fold increase in asparagine.

Further evidence indicating that asparagine may be formed
from aspartate comes from work with cell-free extracts of
wheat germ and lupine seedlings (Webster and Varner, 1955).
Such extracts are able to catalyze the conversation of $C^{14}$-aspar-
tate to $C^{14}$-asparagine. The reaction requires the presence of
ammonium ions, ATP, and magnesium ions. A balance study
has shown that the overall reaction proceeds as follows:

$$\text{Aspartate} + NH_3 + ATP \rightleftharpoons \text{Asparagine} + ADP + P_i$$

This overall reaction is identical to the reaction for glutamine
synthesis. The extracts do not, however, catalyze any detectable formation of aspartyl hydroxamate unless very high concentrations of hydroxylamine are present. This may explain
the failure of Elliott (1951) to detect aspartyl hydroxamate
synthesis.

Thus, it can be seen that at least one mode of asparagine
synthesis may be from aspartate itself. Whether this reaction
is really identical with the reaction for glutamine synthesis,
whether it constitutes a major pathway of asparagine synthesis
in living cells, and whether there are other reactions resulting
in the synthesis of asparagine, are all questions of importance.
It is likely that they will be answered soon.

*Peptide bond synthesis.* Incubation of bean hypocotyls with
glutamate, cysteine, and glycine results in a marked increase

in the glutathione level of the tissues (Webster, 1953). When $C^{14}$-glycine is employed, $C^{14}$-glutathione can be isolated. Glutathione synthesis can also be demonstrated in cell-free extracts of a variety of plants. In addition to the three amino acids, the synthesis requires ATP and both magnesium and potassium ions. Glutathione synthesis in plants, therefore, is very similar to glutathione synthesis in animals (Bloch, 1949; Johnson and Bloch, 1951). Kinetic studies indicate that the dipeptide, glutamylcysteine, is an intermediate in glutathione formation in both animals (Snoke and Bloch, 1952) and plants (Webster, 1953). This thesis is supported by the finding (Webster, 1953) that cell-free extracts capable of forming glutathione can also synthesize glutamylcysteine from glutamate, cysteine, ATP, $Mg^{++}$, and $K^+$. Two separate enzymes have been purified (Webster and Varner, 1954; 1955) from wheat germ extracts which carry out the synthesis of glutathione in the following manner:

Glutamate + cysteine + ATP $\rightleftharpoons$ glutamylcysteine + ADP + $P_i$

Glutamylcysteine + glycine + ATP $\rightleftharpoons$ glutathione + ADP + $P_i$

The properties of the two enzymes have been examined and found to be remarkably similar. Snoke (1955) has purified considerably from yeast the enzyme, glutathione synthetase, which forms glutathione from glutamylcysteine and glycine. Like glutamine synthetase, this enzyme catalyzes transfer reactions dependent upon ADP, phosphate or arsenate, and $Mg^{++}$ or $Mn^{++}$. A similar situation has been observed with glutamylcysteine synthetase (Webster and Varner, 1954) in which the enzyme also catalyzes a glutamyl transfer reaction. These considerations support the suggestion (Webster, 1955) that the mechanism of synthesis of at least some peptide bonds is essentially the same as the mechanism of glutamine synthesis. This is not the case for all peptidic linkages, however. Maas (1952, 1953, 1956), in an elegant series of experiments, has shown that the synthesis of pantothenic acid by an enzyme preparation from *Escherichia coli*:

Pantoate + $\beta$-Alanine + ATP $\rightleftharpoons$

Pantothenate + AMP + Pyrophosphate

actually proceeds in the following manner:

Enzyme (E) + Pantoate + ATP $\rightleftharpoons$

E-Pantoyl-AMP + Pyrophosphate

that is, an anhydride linkage is formed between the carboxyl of pantoate and the phosphate of AMP, the entire structure remaining bound to the enzyme. This "activated" pantoate then reacts with β-alanine, with the consequent liberation of AMP:

E-Pantoyl-AMP + β-Alanine $\rightleftharpoons$ Pantothenate + AMP + E

This type of reaction, in which a carboxyl group is linked to AMP, is identical to the manner of synthesis of acetyl-CoA and various other fatty acid-CoA compounds.

Andreae and coworkers (Andreae and Good, 1955; 1957; Good *et al.*, 1956) have demonstrated the formation of indole-acetyl aspartic acid and indoleacetamide in pea seedlings given indoleacetic acid. The pea seedlings also convert indole-propionic acid, indolebutyric acid, and benzoic acid to indolepropionyl aspartic acid, indolebutyryl aspartic acid, and benzoyl aspartic acid respectively. Good and Andreae (1957) have shown, in addition, that pea seedlings convert trypto-phan to malonyl tryptophan. In each of these instances a peptidic linkage is formed between the carboxyl of the or-ganic acid and the amino group of aspartic or tryptophan. The mechanisms of these syntheses have not been reported as yet, but it would not be surprising if they all proceed by the initial formation of indoleacetyl—or malonyl-CoA, which then reacts with aspartate or tryptophan to form the peptidic linkage. This is the manner of benzoyl glycine synthesis in animals (Schachter and Taggert, 1953). A direct condensation of the acids without the intermediate formation of a CoA compound, such as is found in pantothenate synthesis, is also possible.

It would appear, as a generalization, that those syntheses which result in the liberation of pyrophosphate from ATP involve the intermediate formation of an enzyme-bound acyl-AMP compound, while those syntheses which result in the liberation of orthophosphate from ATP involve the intermediate formation of an enzyme-bound acyl-phosphate compound. The significance of having these two types of reactions to achieve essentially the same end is not clear. However, these two mechanisms appear to represent the two major ways (aside from classical kinase activity) in which ATP promotes biological syntheses. In each case, we are dealing with a type of displacement reaction well known in organic chemistry. Under such circumstances, the activity of ATP in promoting amide and peptide bond synthesis becomes considerably less mysterious. As will be seen in Chapter 4, the knowledge gained through the study of the mechanism of synthesis of simple peptidic linkages has permitted the clarification of the first step in the synthesis of the peptide bonds in protein.

## REFERENCES

ANDREAE, W. A. AND GOOD, N. E., Plant Physiol. **30**, 380 (1955).

ANDREAE, W. A. AND GOOD, N. E., Plant Physiol. **32**, 566 (1957).

BENTLEY, M. AND ABRAMS, R., Federation Proc. **15**, 218 (1956).

BLOCH, K., Jour. Biol. Chem. **179**, 1245 (1949).

BOYER, P. D., KOEPPE, O. J., AND LUCHSINGER, W. W., Jour. Am. Chem. Soc. **78**, 356 (1956).

BRICAS, E. AND FROMAGEOT, C., Adv. in Protein Chem. **8**, 1 (1953).

CHIBNALL, A. C., *Protein Metabolism in the Plant*, Yale University Press (1939).

DEKKER, C. A., STONE, D., AND FRUTON, J. L., Jour. Biol. Chem. **181**, 719 (1949).

ELLIOTT, W. H., Biochem. Jour. **49**, 106 (1951).

ELLIOTT, W. H., Jour. Biol. Chem. **201**, 661 (1953).

GOOD, N. E., ANDREAE, W. A., AND VAN YESSELSTEIN, M. W. H., Plant Physiol. **31**, 231 (1956).

GOOD, N. E. AND ANDREAE, W. A., Plant Physiol. **32**, 561 (1957).

HOPKINS, F. G., Biochem. Jour. **15**, 286 (1921).

KOWALSKY, A., WYTTENBACH, C., LANGER, L., AND KOSHLAND, D. E., JR., Jour. Biol. Chem. **219**, 719 (1956).

JOHNSON, R. B. AND BLOCH, K., Jour. Biol. Chem. **188**, 221 (1951).

LELOIR, L. F. AND CARDINI, C. E., Biochim. Biophys. Acta **12**, 15 (1953).

LEVINTOW, L. AND MEISTER, A., Jour. Biol. Chem. **209**, 265 (1954).

LEVINTOW, L. AND MEISTER, A., Federation Proc. **15**, 299 (1956).

LEVINTOW, L., MEISTER, A., KUFF, E. L., AND HOGEBOOM, G. H., Jour. Am. Chem. Soc. **77**, 5304 (1955).

MAAS, W. K., Jour. Biol. Chem. **198**, 23 (1952).

MAAS, W. K., Federation Proc. **15**, 305 (1956).

MAAS, W. K. AND NOVELLI, G. D., Arch. Biochem. Biophys. **43**, 236 (1953).

MARDASHEV, S. R. AND LESTROVOYA, N. N., Doklady Nauk S.S.S.R. **78**, 547 (1951).

MEISTER, A., *Biochemistry of the Amino Acids*, Academic Press, New York (1957).

MEISTER, A. AND FRASER, P. E., Jour. Biol. Chem. **210**, 37 (1954).

MITCHELL, H. K., SNELL, E. E., AND WILLIAMS, R. J., Jour. Am. Chem. Soc. **66,** 267 (1944).

NAYLOR, A. AND TOLBERT, N. E., Plant Physiol. **30,** (Supplement) (1955).

NELSON, C. D. AND KROTKOV, G., Canadian Jour. Botany **34,** 423 (1956).

PFIFFNER, J. J., CALKINS, D. G., O'DELL, B. L., BLOOM, E. S., BROWN, R. A., CAMPBELL, C. J., AND BIRD, O. D., Science **102,** 228 (1945).

PLATTNER, P. A. AND CLAUSON-KASS, N., Experientia **1,** 195 (1945).

RATNER, S., BLANCHARD, M., COBURN, A. F., AND GREEN, D. E., Jour. Biol. Chem. **155,** 689 (1944).

SCHACHTER, D. AND TAGGERT, J. V., Jour. Biol. Chem. **203,** 925 (1953).

SCHILLING, E. D. AND STRONG, F. M., Jour. Am. Chem. Soc. **77,** 2843 (1955).

SCHROEDER, E. F. AND WOODWARD, G. E., Jour. Biol. Chem. **129,** 283 (1939).

SNOKE, J. E., Jour. Biol. Chem. **213,** 813 (1955).

SNOKE, J. E. AND BLOCH, K., Jour. Biol. Chem. **199,** 407 (1952).

SONNE, J. C., LIN, I., AND BUCHANAN, J. M., Jour. Am. Chem. Soc. **75,** 1516 (1953).

STOLL, A., HOFMANN, A., AND PETRZILKA, T., Helv. Chim. Acta **34,** 1544 (1951).

STUMPF, P. K. AND LOOMIS, W. D., Arch. Biochem. **25,** 451 (1950).

TANRET, C., Compt. rend. **81,** 896 (1875).

VARNER, J. E. AND WEBSTER, G. C., Plant Physiol. **30,** 393 (1955).

VARNER, J. E., SLOCUM, D. H., AND WEBSTER, G. C., Arch. Biochem. Biophys. **73,** 508 (1958).

VIRTANEN, A. I. AND BERG, A. M., Acta Chem. Scand. **8,** 1089 (1954).

WEBSTER, G. C., Arch. Biochem. Biophys. **47,** 241 (1953).

WEBSTER, G. C., Plant Physiol. **28,** 724 (1953).

WEBSTER, G. C., Plant Physiol. **28,** 728 (1953).

WEBSTER, G. C., Plant Physiol. **29,** 382 (1954).

WEBSTER, G. C., Ann. Rev. Plant Physiol. **6,** 43 (1955).

WEBSTER, G. C. AND VARNER, J. E., Arch. Biochem. Biophys. **52,** 22 (1954).

WEBSTER, G. C. AND VARNER, J. E., Arch. Biochem. Biophys. **55,** 95 (1955).

WEBSTER, G. C. AND VARNER, J. E., Jour. Biol. Chem. **215,** 91 (1955).

WEBSTER, G. C. AND VARNER, J. E., Federation Proc. **14,** 301 (1955).

WIELAND, H. AND WITKOP, B., Ann. Chem. **543,** 171 (1940).

WINTERFELD, K. AND RINK, M., Ann. Chem. **561,** 186 (1948).

WOLF, D. E., VALIANT, J., PECK, R. L., AND FOLKERS, K., Jour. Am. Chem. Soc. **74,** 2002 (1952).

YAMAMOTO, Y., Jour. Biochem. (Japan) **42,** 763 (1955).

# Chapter 4

# Protein and
## Nucleic Acid Metabolism

Every cell contains hundreds of different protein molecules. Although each of these molecules is made up of roughly the same 18–20 amino acids, there is increasing evidence that the amino acid sequence of different protein molecules is specified with great accuracy. Thus, we are faced with the problem of learning not only how the peptide bonds of proteins are formed, but also how amino acids are arranged in the specific sequences that are unique for the molecules of different proteins. The enzyme system responsible for the synthesis of a protein molecule, therefore, must be not only a peptide-bond former, but also an information carrier. There are only three types of cellular macromolecules which appear to be capable of acting as information carriers for the synthesis of a specific protein molecule. These are: ribonucleic acid, deoxyribonucleic acid, and protein (or some combination of these three). In the present chapter, the biosynthesis of both protein and nucleic acids, as well as their possible relationship will be discussed principally. A brief consideration of our amazingly meager knowledge of cellular protein degradation is also included.

Research on protein synthesis has followed two major lines of investigation. The first has been concerned with learning as much as possible about the characteristics of the overall protein synthesis process, while the second has attempted the subdivision of the process into its component steps. Each of these lines of endeavor has, of necessity, employed both intact cells and cell-free preparations in decreasing stages of heterogeneity, and each has gained much information on the chemical steps involved in the synthesis of protein molecules (for earlier reviews, see Borsook, 1953; Tarver, 1954; Crook, 1957; Simkin and Work, 1957; Spiegelman, 1957).

## CHARACTERISTICS OF THE
## PROTEIN SYNTHESIS PROCESS

*Amino acids as protein precursors.* If one regards a protein molecule as a typical polymer, then the repeating units in the polymer are obviously the amino acids. The results of a large number of investigations with both plants and animals demonstrate clearly that amino acids (probably in an "activated" form) serve as precursors for protein molecules. For example, in animals, the omission of any single "essential" amino acid (that is, an amino acid that the animal cannot produce itself in sufficient quantity) results in an immediate cessation of protein synthesis and a dramatic decrease in protein levels. This stoppage of protein synthesis occurs even in the presence of all amino acids except the one left out of the diet (Frazier, *et al.*, 1947). Likewise, experiments with amino acid analogues or with isotopes have provided strong evidence for amino acids acting as protein precursors in the synthesis of specific proteins, such as tryptophan peroxidase (Lee and Williams, 1952), antibodies (Green and Anker, 1954), or ferritin (Loftfield and Harris, 1956).

In yeast, Halvorson and Spiegelman (1953) found that the cells contain an internal pool of amino acids. When the cells are induced to synthesize new enzyme protein, the levels of the internal free amino acids decrease. If the internal free amino acid levels are arbitrarily decreased prior to the induction of synthesis, little or no new protein is formed. Likewise, if the synthesis of new protein is prevented by the presence of certain amino acid analogues, net incorporation of amino acids from the internal pool into the protein fraction is prevented (Halvorson and Spiegelman, 1952; Halvorson, *et al.*, 1955). Rotman and Spiegelman (1954) grew *Escherichia coli* cells (which have essentially no internal free amino acid pool) in $C^{14}$-lactate until all cellular constituents were uniformly labeled. The cells were then induced to synthesize the enzyme, β-galactosidase, in the presence of a mixture of unlabeled amino acids. When the enzyme was purified by a combination of starch electrophoresis and specific precipitation with purified antiserum, less than 1% of the enzyme carbon was found to be derived from the overwhelming amount of labeled cellular constituents. The enzyme, instead, had been formed from the unlabeled free amino acids. Almost identical results have been obtained by Monod and coworkers. Further evidence that amino acids are precursors of protein has come from studies with mutant strains of microorganisms which have lost their ability to synthesize a particular amino acid. For example, Monod, *et al.* (1952) tested eleven different amino acid-requiring mutants of *Escherichia coli*, and found in each case that lack of the required amino acid prevents the synthesis of either total cellular protein or the enzyme, β-galactosidase. Similar results have been observed by Rickenberg, *et al.* (1953) and by Ushiba and Magasanik (1952), who showed that the required amino acid could not be replaced by carbon sources and ammonium sulfate. Thus, the evidence seems quite definite that amino acids are indeed protein precursors, and it is likely that this is the case in all organisms.

Evidence that amino acids are not protein precursors is difficult to find. Steward, *et al.* (1956) have reported that when $C^{14}$-glucose and $C^{14}$-glutamine are supplied to tissue cultures of carrot roots, the specific activities of protein glutamate, aspartate, and alanine are higher with $C^{14}$-glucose than with $C^{14}$-glutamine. The results could be due to some metabolites other than free amino acids serving as precursors of protein in tissue culture cells. However, if the internal pool of available glucose is relatively small, while the internal pool of available glutamine is relatively large, the results they report could be obtained. Likewise, if the conversion of glucose into various amino acids is rapid compared with the conversion of glutamine, glucose could appear to be a more efficient precursor. Alternately, as long as the magnitudes of the internal pools of available glucose and glutamine are unknown, the results obtained could be influenced strongly by the rates of penetration of the metabolites into the cells. One must conclude that the available evidence is still overwhelmingly in favor of the concept that proteins are formed from amino acids.

*Need for the simultaneous presence of all amino acids.* Although not conclusive, evidence is appearing in support of the view that optimal utilization of amino acids for protein synthesis requires that all amino acids be available at approximately the same time. In animals, Geiger (1947, 1950) has observed that all essential amino acids must be fed within a very short time period if protein synthesis is to occur. If any one essential amino acid is fed more than a short time either before or after the others, no protein synthesis occurs. As the feeding of incomplete amino acid mixtures results in the increased excretion of amino acids, it appears that an animal forms protein if all amino acids are present, but excretes the amino acids if all amino acids are not present. Similar evidence is much more difficult to obtain in plants because of their capacity for the synthesis of amino acids. However, bacteria which lack the ability to form a particular amino acid must have that amino acid supplied (even in the presence of all other amino acids) for protein synthesis to occur. Likewise, Gale and Folkes (1953) have found that total protein synthesis in *Staphylococcus aureus* proceeds at maximal rates only in the presence of all of the component amino acids (Figure 18). Omission of one or more amino acids results in the decrease or elimination of protein formation. These results suggest the need for all amino acids to be present at about the same time for protein synthesis in plants as in animals.

*Specificity.* Extensive studies have demonstrated that every living tissue examined will, under normal conditions, incorporate into its proteins any amino acid that is a normal constituent of the proteins (Borsook, 1953). The rate of incorporation varies with both the tissue and the amino acid, but is roughly proportional to the amount of the amino acid occurring in the protein (or proteins) being formed, and to the rate of cellular protein synthesis. The fact that amino acid sequences in various proteins have been found to be highly specific leads one to expect that only those amino acids which normally occur in protein can be incorporated into protein. This expectation is borne out by the observations that D-amino acids and some amino acids which are not normal protein constituents (α-aminobutyric, γ-aminobutyric, and α-aminoadipic acids, for example) have not been found to be

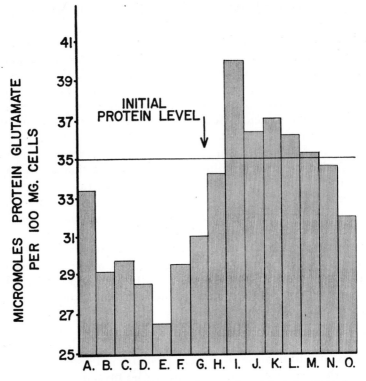

Figure 18. Amino acid requirements for protein synthesis by *Staphylococcus aureus* cells. Bars indicate the increase or decrease in protein glutamate after 30 minutes at 38° C. in the presence of:

A. Glucose.

B. Glucose plus glutamate.

C. Glucose, aspartate, and glutamate.

D. Glucose, arginine, and glutamate.

E. Glucose, alanine, aspartate, cysteine, and glutamate.

F. Glucose, arginine, glutamate, lysine, methionine, and proline.

G. Glucose, alanine, aspartate, cysteine, glutamate, glycine, leucine, phenylalanine, tryptophan, tyrosine, and valine.

H. Glucose, alanine, aspartate, cysteine, glutamate, glycine, leucine, phenylalanine, serine, threonine, tryptophan, tyrosine, valine.

I. Glucose, alanine, arginine, aspartate, cysteine, glutamate, glycine, histidine, isoleucine, leucine, lysine, methionine, phenlyalanine, proline, serine, threonine, tryptophan, tyrosine, and valine.

J. Same as I., but without aspartate.

K. Same as I., but without arginine.

L. Same as I., but without phenylalanine and tyrosine.

M. Same as I., but without histidine.

N. Same as I., but without cysteine.

O. Same as I., but without cysteine and methionine.

Adapted from the data of Gale and Folkes (1953a).

TABLE VIII

Incorporation of "Unnatural" Amino Acids into Proteins

| Amino acid | Organism | Reference |
|---|---|---|
| Azatryptophan | E. coli | Pardee, et al., 1956. |
| Ethionine | Rat | Gross and Tarver, 1955. |
| Ethionine | Tetrahymena | Tarver, 1955. |
| p-Fluorophenylalanine | L. arabinosus | Baker, et al., 1954. |
| Seleno-methionine | E. coli | Cohen and Cowie, 1957. |
| β-Thienylalanine | Yeast | Dittmer, 1957. |

incorporated into protein (Borsook, 1953; Borsook, et al., 1950). However, recent studies have indicated that the protein synthesis mechanism may not be completely specific. As is noted in Table VIII, ethionine has been found to be incorporated into the proteins of both rats and Tetrahymena. Azatryptophan is incorporated into the proteins of Escherichia coli, and, if the bacterial cells are infected with bacteriophage $T_2$, the azatryptophan is incorporated into the bacteriophage protein. In addition, p-fluorophenylalanine is incorporated into the proteins of Lactobacillus arabinosus, while β-thienylalanine is incorporated into the proteins of yeast. In this latter instance, it was found that $C^{14}$-β-thienylalanine is incorporated equally well into the proteins of the various cellular fractions, in vivo (Dittmer, 1957). This suggests that we are probably not dealing with incorporation into a single abnormal protein. Especially striking are the observations of Cohen and Cowie (1957) that seleno-methionine is incorporated into the proteins of Escherichia coli. In the case of a methionine-requiring mutant, the bacterium grows at normal rates on seleno-methionine. The incorporation of such "unnatural" amino acids into protein, in vivo, is extremely interesting and deserves much more attention. The results obtained thus far, however, certainly raise a question as to how discriminating the protein-forming mechanism may be.

*Necessity for an energy source.* Altough there are numerous reports in the literature that respiratory inhibitors and dinitrophenol inhibit protein synthesis, these findings do not provide conclusive evidence that the inhibitors act on protein synthesis itself. For example, it has been found that the absorption of amino acids by plant (Webster, 1954), animal (Christiansen, 1954), and bacterial (Gale, 1953) cells requires respiratory energy, so the inhibitions observed could reflect the inhibition of amino acid uptake by intact cells. Spiegelman, *et al.* (1947), however, have provided convincing evidence that protein synthesis itself requires respiratory energy. As stated earlier, the synthesis of new enzyme molecules during induced enzyme formation in yeast utilizes the pool of free amino acids in the cells. Thus, we have a conversion of amino acids into protein without the amino acids having to pass into the cell from the outside. Spiegelman, *et al.* (1947) found that this utilization of internal amino acids for protein synthesis is strongly inhibited by respiratory inhibitors and, most significantly, by inhibitors of oxidative phosphorylation.

*Necessity of nucleic acid for protein synthesis.* The early microscopic studies of Caspersson (1947) and Brachet (1952) showed that high cellular concentrations of nucleic acid often could be correlated with active protein synthesis. Similar results have been obtained in the extensive investigations of Gale and Folkes (1953) who found that the rate of protein synthesis in *Staphylococcus aureus* cells varies with the nucleic acid content. Likewise, Oota and Osawa (1954) observed that the rate of protein synthesis in bean seedlings varies directly with the content of microsomal ribonucleic acid. Brachet (1954), utilizing the observation (Kaufman and Das, 1953) that ribonuclease penetrates into root tips, showed that treatment of onion roots with ribonuclease results in a strong inhibition of amino acid incorporation into protein, without affecting respiration at all. It has not been possible to perform similar experiments in most other organisms, presumably because ribonuclease cannot penetrate into all living cells. Ribonuclease can, however, enter intact cells of *Bacillus megaterium*, or protoplasts prepared from these cells, and in both of these instances strong inhibitions of protein synthesis have been observed (Landman and Spiegelman, 1955; Groth, 1956). Deoxyribonuclease, in contrast, does not inhibit enzyme formation in intact *B. megaterium* cells. Landman and Spiegelman (1955) report, in fact, that deoxyribonuclease frequently enhances enzyme synthesis. When protoplasts of *B. megaterium* are treated to remove only deoxyribonucleic acid, no inhibition of enzyme synthesis results. Extensive removal of deoxyribonucleic acid produces a concomitant loss of ribonucleic acid, however, with a resultant inhibition of protein synthesis. The findings suggest that intact molecules of ribonucleic acid are essential for enzyme synthesis in *B. megaterium*, but that deoxyribonucleic acid may not be as directly concerned.

The evidence that nucleic acid is necessary for protein synthesis raises a question as to the manner in which it participates in the synthetic process. In this connection, Gale and Folkes (1955c) observed that the synthesis of β-galactosidase by *Staphylococcus aureus* cells requires the presence of a mixture of purine and pyrimidine bases. Furthermore, as can be seen in Figure 19, synthesis of total protein in these cells, while not exhibiting an absolute requirement for the bases, nevertheless is markedly promoted by the purine-pyrimidine mixture. Pardee (1954), while investigating the synthesis of β-galactosidase in uracil-requiring mutants of *E. coli*, found that enzyme synthesis occurs only in the presence of added uracil. If the supply of uracil is limiting, enzyme synthesis stops as soon as the uracil supply is exhausted. Similar results have been observed by Spiegelman, *et al.* (1954) with both uracil- and adenine-requiring mutants of *E. coli*. Moreover, depletion of the nucleotide pool of yeast cells inhibits their ability to form enzymes, but the ability is restored by a purine-pyrimidine mixture (Spiegelman, *et al.*, 1954). These results have led to the important postulate that protein synthesis requires the concurrent synthesis of nucleic acid. Whether the synthesis of both ribonucleic and deoxyribonucleic acid is necessary for the synthesis of certain proteins is not yet certain. Numerous investigators, however, have reported that selective inhibition of deoxyribonucleic acid formation by x-ray or other treatments has no effect on the ability of an organism to form at least some proteins (Baron, *et al.*, 1953;

Kelner, 1953; Sher and Malette, 1954; Halvorson and Jackson, 1956). Furthermore, Cohen and Barner (1954) have observed that a thymine-requiring mutant of *E. coli* can form the enzyme, xylose isomerase, in the absence of added thymine. These findings certainly raise a question as to the direct participation of deoxyribonucleic acid in protein synthesis (especially enzyme synthesis) in a manner analogous to the participation of ribonucleic acid. However, they do not rule out the need for deoxyribonucleic acid, or its synthesis, for the synthesis of specific proteins (in the nucleus, for example).

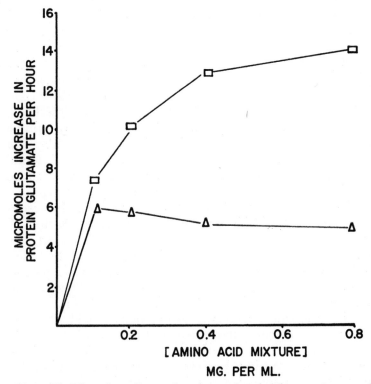

Figure 19. Effect of a mixture of purines and pyrimidines on the rate of protein synthesis by *Staphylococcus aureus* as a function of amino acid concentration. Squares: purine-pyrimidine mixture; triangles: control. Adapted from the data of Gale and Folkes (1953b).

If ribonucleic acid synthesis is indeed necessary for the synthesis of protein, then one would expect: (a) that induction of protein synthesis would be reflected in increased synthesis of at least some kinds of ribonucleic acid, and (b) that inhibition of nucleic acid synthesis would also inhibit protein synthesis. Little definite information is available concerning these possibilities. Chantrenne (1956) has observed that the oxygen-induced syntheses of cytochrome c, cytochrome peroxidase, and catalase in resting yeast cells all result in increased incorporation of adenine and uracil into specific fractions of cellular ribonucleic acid. Interestingly, the incorporation also occurs when the inducer is added, but enzyme synthesis is seemingly blocked with p-fluorophenylalanine. However, it is not known whether p-fluorophenylalanine actually stops the synthesis of protein molecules here, or whether an inactive protein containing p-fluorophenylalanine is formed. In attempts to inhibit nucleic acid synthesis, various investigators (Spiegelman, *et al.*, 1954; Creaser, 1955) have observed that a number of different purine or pyrimidine analogues inhibit protein synthesis. Unfortunately, they have not established whether the analogues actually inhibit ribonucleic acid synthesis itself. It has been found, in fact, that several of these analogues, especially 8-azaguanine, are incorporated into ribonucleic acid by living cells (Matthews, 1954; Lasnitzki, *et al.*, 1954; Matthews and Smith, 1956; Mitchell, *et al.*, 1950; Heinrich, *et al.*, 1952). It may be that the analogues inhibit protein synthesis by forming an "abnormal" ribonucleic acid which cannot act metabolically. Obviously, experiments on the incorporation of either purines or their analogues into ribonucleic acid offer excellent beginnings for further study of the manner in which ribonucleic acid participates in protein synthesis. It might be noted here that the ready incorporation of either amino acid analogues into protein or purine analogues into nucleic acid suggests that both synthetic mechanisms will accept an unnatural precursor. In view of this, the question might be raised as to how often the cell spontaneously produces an abnormal macromolecule, and what effects such abnormalities have on normal cellular growth.

TABLE IX

Effect of Chloramphenicol on Protein and Nucleic Acid Synthesis

| System | Chloramphenicol concentration (M) | Per cent inhibition | | Reference |
|---|---|---|---|---|
| | | Protein synthesis | Nucleic acid synthesis | |
| S. aureus cells | $3 \times 10^{-5}$ | 100. | 0. | Gale and Folkes (1953). |
| E. coli cells | $1 \times 10^{-5}$ | 94. | 30. | Pardee and Prestidge (1956). |
| A. vinelandii cells | $1 \times 10^{-4}$ | 86. | 63. | Bernlohr and Webster (1958). |
| Ehrlich ascites tumor cells | $8 \times 10^{-3}$ | 33. | 50. | LePage (1953). |
| Calf thymus nuclei | $3.6 \times 10^{-3}$ | 55. | 50. | Breitman and Webster (1958). |
| Pea seedling microsomes | $5 \times 10^{-4}$ | 95. | 93. | Webster (1957d). |

*"Uncoupling"* *of protein and nucleic acid synthesis.* Although the evidence discussed above supports the view that protein synthesis requires the concurrent synthesis of nucleic acid, the question arises as to whether nucleic acid synthesis requires the coincident synthesis of protein. The earliest evidence on this point was obtained by Levy, *et al.* (1949) who found that cobalt ions inhibit growth (and therefore protein synthesis) of at least one bacterial species without inhibiting ribonucleic acid synthesis. Similar results have been obtained with the antibiotic, Chloramphenicol (Gale and Folkes, 1953; Wisseman, *et al.*, 1954; Pardee and Prestidge, 1956). Chloramphenicol, in low concentrations, completely inhibits protein synthesis in *Staphylococcus aureus* without inhibiting ribonucleic acid synthesis (Table IX). These results are reminiscent of the classical findings of Loomis and Lipmann (1948) that respiration and phosphorylation can be "uncoupled" with dinitrophenol. The formation of ribonucleic acid, therefore, does not necessarily require the concurrent synthesis of protein, and may be "uncoupled" experimentally from protein synthesis. Whether the ribonucleic acid formed as a result of Chloramphenicol action is identical to ribonucleic acid formed in connection with protein synthesis is not as yet known, although Pardee and Prestidge (1956) have found no change in the base ratios of nucleic acid formed in the presence of Chloramphenicol. The "uncoupling" apparently does not occur in *Azotobacter vinelandii,* where both nucleic acid and protein syntheses are inhibited, or in certain other systems (Table IX).

As an extension of the above results, Pardee and Prestidge (1956) have made several important observations concerning the manner in which ribonucleic acid is formed in bacterial cells. They find:

a. Inhibition of protein synthesis results in similar inhibition of ribonucleic acid synthesis.
b. In amino acid-requiring mutants of *E. coli,* ribonucleic acid synthesis cannot occur in the absence of amino acids.
c. Even when ribonucleic acid synthesis is "uncoupled"

from protein synthesis by Chloramphenicol, the synthesis of ribonucleic acid in amino acid-requiring *E. coli* mutants requires the presence of traces of the necessary amino acids.

The authors conclude that ribonucleic acid synthesis normally proceeds in conjunction with protein synthesis, but if these processes are "uncoupled" by Chloramphenicol, then nucleic acid synthesis still requires the presence of a complete amino acid mixture. This suggests that protein and nucleic acid syntheses may be coupled through the formation of a common intermediate, or that amino acids are somehow required for nucleic acid formation. It may be that Chloramphenicol acts by specifically inhibiting peptide bond formation in proteins.

*Summary.* The results of the investigations cited above, in which intact cells of a variety of plants have been used as experimental material, have elucidated a number of characteristics of protein synthesis. The salient features of the overall process of protein synthesis are as follows:

a. Protein is formed in a process in which free amino acids are condensed together without the formation of detectable peptide intermediates. All of the amino acids composing a protein are needed at about the same time in the synthetic process.
b. Respiratory energy is required for protein synthesis.
c. Intact molecules of nucleic acid are likewise necessary for protein synthesis. In addition, an increasing volume of evidence supports the view that protein synthesis requires the concurrent synthesis of nucleic acid, and that the two syntheses normally are coupled together in some manner. They can be uncoupled, however, in a few cases, by substances which allow nucleic acid synthesis to occur while inhibiting protein synthesis.
d. Finally, the mechanism of either protein or nucleic acid synthesis is not completely selective, and allows certain "abnormal" amino acids or purines to be incorporated into protein or nucleic acid.

## STUDIES ON PROTEIN SYNTHESIS
## IN PREPARATIONS OF DISRUPTED CELLS

The information discussed in the preceding section shows that our knowledge of protein synthesis has been increased tremendously by studies with various kinds of intact cells. The important results obtained have raised even more important questions concerning the actual chemical pathways involved in transforming amino acids into specific proteins. Unfortunately, the answers to such questions do not appear to be obtainable with intact cells. The design of experiments in which intact cells are employed to study the mechanisms of protein synthesis has become increasingly difficult, and the interpretation of results obtained (due to permeability factors, enzyme action at the cell membrane, competing reactions, changing substrate pools and their effect on metabolic pathways, etc.) is even more difficult. Disruption of a cell results in a considerable disorganization of cellular structure. Yet, despite this disorganization of the cell as a whole, many cellular entities (nuclei, mitochondria, etc.) remain intact and metabolically active. Employment of disrupted cells and isolated cellular bodies as experimental systems has increased our knowledge of carbohydrate and fat metabolism in a manner unattainable with intact cells. It is not surprising, therefore, that similar techniques have been adopted for the study of protein synthesis.

*Net protein synthesis in preparations of disrupted cells.* The question of whether disrupted cells continue to carry on a net synthesis of protein was first investigated by Gale and Folkes (1955a). They found that disrupted *Staphylococcus aureus* cells exhibit as much as a 10% increase in total protein (as determined by micro-Kjeldahl) when incubated in the presence of a mixture of amino acids and hexose diphosphate. Similar results have been obtained by Webster (1957d) with disrupted pea seedlings. In this case, the protein increase (as determined simultaneously by three different methods) is almost entirely in a nucleoprotein fraction. Some properties of this *in vitro* protein synthesis system are presented in Table X. It can be seen that the requirements for synthesis are simi-

## TABLE X

Net Protein Synthesis by a Nucleoprotein Fraction from Pea Seedlings[1]

| System | Micrograms protein formed per milligram protein per hour |
|---|---|
| Complete | 58. |
| minus amino acid mixture | 0. |
| minus adenosine triphosphate | 15. |
| minus magnesium ions | 25. |
| minus potassium ions | 38. |
| plus p-fluorophenylalanine | 23. |
| plus ribonuclease | 0. |

[1] Adapted from Webster (1957).

lar to those for protein synthesis in intact cells (amino acids, energy source, nucleic acid). The maximum amount of protein formed in this system is very small, amounting to about 8% of the original protein of the nucleoprotein fraction.

Considerably greater amounts of protein synthesis have been observed in other experimental systems. Spiegelman (1957) has found that a sediment obtained when *B. megaterium* protoplasts are disrupted by osmotic shock exhibits a *several-fold* increase in total protein and nucleic acid when incubated with an amino acid mixture, ATP, HDP, and metal ions. This striking increase is far greater than has been obtained hitherto with any other experimental system. As might be expected, the system must be prepared very carefully in order to retain its activity.

A further indication of net protein synthesis in disrupted cell preparations has been obtained by Gale and Folkes (1955b) in an investigation of enzyme formation by disrupted *Staphylococcus aureus* cells. They have reported that the activities of catalase and "glucozymase" (the enzyme system producing acid from glucose) increase several-fold in the presence of an amino acid mixture, ATP, and HDP. If an inducer is present, the enzyme, β-galactosidase, is likewise formed. The increase in enzyme activity is eliminated if one of the components of the reaction system is omitted. Enzyme development is strongly inhibited by Chloramphenicol, a known inhibitor of protein synthesis in intact cells, and by treatment of the preparations with ribonuclease or deoxyribonuclease. If the disrupted cells are extracted with 1 M sodium chloride, the activity is either lost or greatly inhibited, but can be restored by adding bacterial RNA, DNA, or a mixture of purines and pyrimidines to the extracted preparation (Figure 20). It is evident that different additions affect each enzyme development differently, suggesting that the synthesis of some enzymes is linked to ribonucleic acid, some to deoxyribonucleic acid, and some to the formation of polynucleotide. These observations are very provocative and deserve much further investigation, for they provide a means by which the synthesis of specific proteins might be linked to specific nucleic acids. This is especially the case now that nucleic acid preparations can be separated into numerous individual nucleic acids or groups of nucleic acids by column chromatography (Bendich, et al., 1955).

*Amino acid incorporation into protein.* Obviously, the employment of suitably sensitive assay techniques and highly active preparations allows the net synthesis of protein to be detected and measured in disrupted cell preparations. In addition, numerous investigators have studied the incorporation of labeled amino acids into protein. This is an important technique, and its employment is essential to the elucidation of the mechanism of protein synthesis. In the case of both intact cells and cell-free preparations, the labeled amino acids can be incorporated into protein as a result of the formation of new protein molecules. However, the possibility exists that amino acids might be incorporated, either in intact cells or cell-free preparations, by any of several other processes:

a. The addition of the labeled amino acid to the N-terminal or C-terminal end of a protein molecule.
b. The exchange of a labeled amino acid for the same amino acid at the end of a protein molecule.
c. The exchange of a labeled amino acid for the same amino acid in the interior of a protein molecule (presumably by some process involving the partial reversal of protein synthesis.

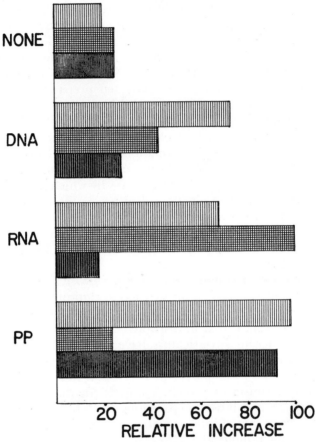

Figure 20. Factors affecting development of several enzyme activities after their elimination by extraction of disrupted *Staphylococcus aureus* cells with 1 M NaCl. Each system contained ATP, hexose diphosphate, and a mixture of amino acids.

Top Bar: "glucozymase"

Middle Bar: catalase

Lower Bar: beta-galactosidase

Additions are: deoxyribonucleic acid (DNA), ribonucleic acid (RNA), purine-pyrimidine mixture (PP). Adapted from the data of Gale and Folkes (1955b).

Of these possibilities, the first must be considered most seriously, as Cornwell and Luck (1958) have presented evidence that incubation of certain purified proteins with labeled amino acids sometimes results in a binding of a small amount of the amino acid to the protein. Such "incorporation," however, as well as incorporation by the two exchange processes listed above, can be differentiated from the incorporation resulting from protein synthesis by several criteria. Incorporation by binding or exchange should not be dependent upon respiratory energy, the presence of other amino acids, or the presence of nucleic acid.

Although the results of Cornwell and Luck (1958) clearly demonstrate that amino acids can bind to proteins under certain conditions, evidence for amino acid incorporation into protein as a result of exchange reactions is difficult to find. Gale and Folkes (1955a) have suggested that glutamate, in the absence of other amino acids, is incorporated into *Staphylococcus aureus* protein by an exchange process, but their results neither establish this point unequivocally, nor tell us whether the glutamate is located: (a) throughout the protein molecules, (b) only on the terminal ends, or (c) in conjunction with some glutamate-containing molecule (such as glutathione) that is associated with certain protein molecules.

Actually, exchange reactions associated with protein synthesis are of great potential aid in elucidating the mechanism of protein synthesis, but the possibility of real exchange reactions associated with the protein-forming machinery has received little attention. Unfortunately, failure to observe net protein synthesis during amino acid incorporation into protein often has been interpreted to mean that the amino acids are being incorporated by an exchange mechanism. Such conclusions are without foundation. Protein levels depend upon the ratio of synthesis rate to degradation rate, while amino acid incorporation (due to protein synthesis) depends only on the synthesis rate. Thus, amino acid incorporation, which is entirely the result of the synthesis of new protein, could occur under any of the following circumstances:

a. The rate of protein synthesis exceeds the rate of protein breakdown. Protein level increases during amino acid incorporation.
b. The rate of protein synthesis equals the rate of protein breakdown. Protein level remains unchanged during amino acid incorporation.
c. The rate of protein synthesis is less than the rate of protein breakdown. Protein level decreases during amino acid incorporation.

Therefore, depending on the rate of protein degradation, one could have equal amounts of amino acid incorporation (resulting from equal amounts of actual protein synthesis) while the protein level of the system was increasing, unchanged, or decreasing. Failure to measure net protein synthesis does not constitute proof either that new protein molecules are not being formed, or that amino acid incorporation is caused by exchange reactions. It is far more important to know whether the characteristics of the process of amino acid incorporation into protein resemble those of cellular protein synthesis. The results of many investigations, with both intact cells and cell-free extracts, have shown that amino acid incorporation exhibits the same (or very similar) characteristics as does actual protein synthesis. In addition, the study of amino acid incorporation by various cell-free preparations has uncovered considerable additional information on the characteristics of both amino acid incorporation and protein synthesis.

*Amino acid incorporation by cell-free extracts.* Many preparations of disrupted cells have been found to be highly active in the incorporation of amino acids into protein. For example, Lester (1953, 1955) observed that lysis of *Micrococcus lysodeikticus* cells with lysozyme (in the presence of sucrose) yields cell-free preparations capable of incorporating $C^{14}$-leucine into their protein at rates somewhat higher than have been obtained in preparations of mammalian tissues. Similar results have been obtained by Gale and Folkes (1955a) with cells of *Staphylococcus aureus* disrupted by sonic vibration. Cellular disruption of several different higher plants in the

TABLE XI

Properties of the Amino Acid Incorporation System of Various Disrupted Cell Preparations

| Treatment | Relative incorporation of amino acid into protein | | | |
| --- | --- | --- | --- | --- |
| | Staphylococcus aureus | Micrococcus lysodeikticus | Pea seedlings | Liver microsomes |
| None | 1.00 | 1.00 | 1.00 | 1.00 |
| Plus ATP | 0.98 | 0.70 | 2.19+ | 1.63+ |
| Plus HDP | 1.75 | — | 1.15 | — |
| Plus ATP and HDP | 3.00 | — | 3.39 | 3.50 |
| Plus ATP, HDP, and amino acid mixture | 8.33 | 4.89++ | 4.95 | 3.50 |
| Pretreated with ribonuclease | 0.69 | 0.04 | 0.51 | 0.01 |
| Pretreated with deoxyribonuclease | 0.64 | 4.54 | 0.98 | — |

+ After removal of endogenous ATP from the preparation.
++ Amino acid mixture only. No ATP or HDP.

presence of sucrose also yields preparations that are active in the incorporation of amino acids into protein (Webster, 1955; Stephenson, *et al.*, 1956). General properties of some of the disrupted preparations are summarized in Table XI, and compared with a preparation from mammalian cells. The plant preparations exhibit a similar requirement for the presence of a mixture of amino acids in order to have incorporation of any one amino acid at maximal rates. Incorporation by all preparations is inhibited in a striking manner by ribonuclease and, in some cases, by deoxyribonuclease.

The requirement for respiratory energy for protein synthesis in intact cells can be demonstrated with disrupted cells to be due to a specific requirement for adenosine triphosphate, a known product of cellular respiration. Neither adenosine diphosphate nor adenosine monophosphate can substitute effectively for adenosine triphosphate. In fact, adenosine diphosphate is decidedly inhibitory. Guanosine triphosphate, inosine triphosphate, cytidine triphosphate, or uridine triphosphate likewise cannot replace adenosine triphosphate to any significant extent.

The necessity of adenosine triphosphate for amino acid incorporation into protein suggests that magnesium ions are also necessary. This is indeed the case in pea seedling preparations where magnesium ions enhance glutamate-$C^{14}$ incorporation into protein while manganese, calcium, cobalt, zinc, copper, and barium ions are inhibitory (Webster, 1955). Amino acid incorporation by disrupted *Staphylococcus aureus* cells likewise requires magnesium ions (Gale and Folkes, 1955). Amino acid incorporation by pea seedling preparations is also affected by monovalent ions. As can be seen from Table XII, potassium ions markedly enhance amino acid incorporation into protein. Sodium, lithium, and ammonium ions have little effect, and rubidium ions are inhibitory. The enhancement of amino acid incorporation specifically by potassium ions is similar to the necessity of potassium ions for the synthesis of simple peptides (Snoke, *et al.*, 1953; Webster and Varner, 1954). The observations of an enhancement of protein synthesis in potato disks (Steward and Preston, 1941) and bac-

TABLE XII

Effects of Monovalent Cations on Amino Acid
Incorporation by Pea Seedling Preparations[1]

| Cation added | Micromoles glutamate incorporated into protein |
|---|---|
| None | 1.57 |
| Potassium | 2.38 |
| Sodium | 1.50 |
| Lithium | 1.48 |
| Ammonium | 1.45 |
| Rubidium | 0.75 |

[1] Adapted from Webster (1956).

terial protoplasts (Landman and Spiegelman, 1955) by potassium ions may be reflections of a necessity of potassium ions for the formation of the peptide bonds of protein molecules.

*Effects of nucleotides on amino acid incorporation into protein.* As was discussed earlier, Gale and Folkes (1955b) found that the development of some enzyme activities is promoted by ribonucleic acid, others by deoxyribonucleic acid, and still others by a mixture of adenine, guanine, cytosine, and uracil. When nucleic acids are removed from disrupted *Staphylococcus aureus* cells by treatment with deoxyribonuclease, ribonuclease, or by extraction with 1 M sodium chloride, the incorporation of $C^{14}$-glutamate into protein is strongly inhibited. Like enzyme development, the ability to incorporate $C^{14}$-amino acids into protein can be restored by the addition of *Staphylococcal* deoxyribonucleic or ribonucleic acids. The restoration of activity is apparently specific for *Staphylococcus* nucleic acids, as thymus, herring roe, and wheat germ deoxyribonucleic acids as well as beef liver ribonucleic acid are all inactive (Gale, 1954). Deoxyribonucleic acid is somewhat more effective at restoring incorporation activity than ribonucleic acid. Surprisingly, the efficiencies of the two nucleic acids are the same, regardless of the method used to remove nucleic acid; that is, deoxyribonucleic acid will restore activity removed by ribonuclease and ribonucleic acid will restore activity removed by deoxyribonuclease. A mixture of purines and pyrimidines is ineffective in restoring activity. These results, in which the reactivating effect is seemingly specific for *Staphylococcus* nucleic acid, but not specific for the kind of nucleic acid raise many questions concerning the mode of action of the nucleic acids in restoring activity, and require much investigation.

Somewhat different results have been obtained with cell-free extracts of pea seedlings (Webster and Johnson, 1955). Here, the incorporation of $C^{14}$-glutamate is inhibited by pretreatment of the preparation by ribonuclease, but not by deoxyribonuclease. Reactivation of the incorporation system is not specific for pea seedling ribonucleic acid, but instead is produced by any ribonucleic acid preparation. Furthermore, promotion of amino acid incorporation is greater if the ribonucleic acid molecule has been hydrolyzed to its constituent nucleotides. These results suggest, then, that the apparent need for added ribonucleic acid in pea seedling preparations is actually a need for ribonucleotides or related compounds which the cell-free extract can produce from ribonucleic acid. A systematic investigation of the ability of various ribonucleotides and related compounds to promote $C^{14}$-glutamate incorporation into protein (Figure 21) reveals that the most effective compounds are nucleoside-5′-phosphates (Webster and Johnson, 1955; Webster, 1957d). As nucleoside-5′-phosphates are highly efficient precursors of ribonucleic acid in both plant (Webster, 1957c,d) and animal (Goldwasser, 1955; Potter, *et al.*, 1956; Heidelberger, *et al.*, 1956; Canellakis, 1957) preparations, the promotion of amino acid incorporation by nucleoside-5′-phosphates may be due to their acting as efficient precursors of ribonucleic acid (the synthesis of ribonucleic acid presumably being necessary for protein synthesis). In line with this, certain purine analogues or other inhibitors of nucleic acid synthesis (such as 4-aminofolic acid) have been found to inhibit the incorporation of glutamate into the proteins of cell-free extracts of pea seedlings (Figure 22). These findings, therefore, are in agreement with the conclusions derived from experiments with intact cells, that protein synthesis is somehow related to nucleic acid synthesis.

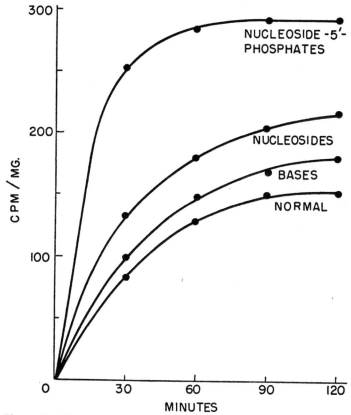

Figure 21. Effects of nucleotides and related substances on $C^{14}$-glutamate incorporation into the proteins of disrupted pea seedlings. Each system contained a mixture of the four nucleotides, nucleosides, or bases commonly found in ribonucleic acid.

Similar systematic studies on the effects of various nucleotides on amino acid incorporation by disrupted *Staphylococcus aureus* cells have not been reported as yet. Burma and Burris (1957), however, have prepared a centrifugal fraction from *Azotobacter vinelandii* cells (disrupted by sonic vibration) which appears to be similar to that prepared from *Staphylococcus aureus*. In agreement with the results with pea seedling preparations, amino acid incorporation by the

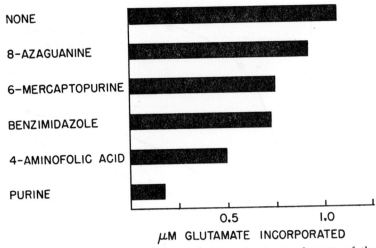

Figure 22. Inhibition by purine analogues and related substances of the incorporation of $C^{14}$-glutamate into the proteins of disrupted pea seedlings.

Azotobacter preparation is promoted to the greatest extent by nucleoside-5′-triphosphates. Some very interesting results have been obtained by Gale and Folkes (1955c), who examined the effects of various nucleotide fractions (obtained by chromatography of a ribonuclease digest of ribonucleic acid) on amino acid incorporation by disrupted *Staphylococcus aureus* cells. Although early results indicated that certain dinucleotides or trinucleotides specifically promoted the incorporation of a given amino acid into protein, further purification of the nucleotide fractions has revealed that the promoting factors are non-nucleotide in nature, and can be separated from the small polynucleotides (Gale, 1956). This would agree with the finding of Webster (1957d) that various dinucleotides and trinucleotides, which have been purified from a ribonuclease digest by column chromatography, are incapable of promoting amino acid incorporation by pea seedling preparations. Little is known about the factors discovered by Gale (1956), but their apparent specificity and high activity make them impressive subjects for further investigation.

We see, therefore, that mononucleotides, polynucleotides,

and non-nucleotide substances associated with polynucleotides all exert powerful influences on amino acid incorporation into protein by different preparations. Both the substance involved and its action differ so greatly with different preparations, however, that it seems impossible to account for the various actions by any single hypothesis. In particular, it would seem especially dangerous to regard the results simply as manifestations of a connection between nucleic acids or nucleic acid synthesis, and protein synthesis.

*Amino acid incorporation by various cellular fractions.* Like intact cells, cell-free extracts possess the disadvantage of bewildering complexity. It is not surprising, therefore, that investigators have attempted to separate the major components of a cell-free extract into those active in protein synthesis and those possessing only confusing side-reactions. The separation of bacterial extracts into components by centrifugation has been unrewarding, the only fraction active *in vitro* in the incorporation of amino acids into protein being a very complex and heavy nucleoprotein material attached to cell walls. Such material may consist of cellular membrane fragments, but has resisted purification.

When a higher plant or animal, with a highly organized cellular structure, is allowed to incorporate an amino acid into protein, it enters the protein of all cellular fractions (Figure 23). The particulates generally become more highly labeled than the "soluble" protein, and thus, nuclear, mitochondrial, and especially microsomal preparations all provide potential experimental systems for the study of amino acid incorporation into protein. Amino acid incorporation by each of these cellular fractions has been investigated to a greater or lesser extent with preparations from both plants and animals, and the results obtained are summarized briefly below:

*Nuclei.* In the intact cell, nuclei readily incorporate amino acids into protein (Borsook, 1953), although in bean seedling cells (Webster, 1954b) the rate of incorporation is considerably less than in other particulate fractions (Table XIII). Amino acid incorporation by isolated nuclei has been studied

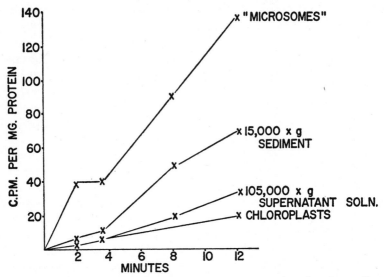

Figure 23. Incorporation of $C^{14}$-leucine into the proteins of various cellular fractions of tobacco leaf disks. Adapted from Stephenson, *et al.* (1956).

TABLE XIII

Distribution of $C^{14}$-Glutamate in Various Cellular
Fractions of Intact Seedlings[1]

| Cellular fraction | Micromoles glutamate per gm. protein per hour | |
| --- | --- | --- |
| | Bean seedlings (3 days old) | Pea seedlings (5 days old) |
| Nuclear | 0.15 | 0.41 |
| Mitochondrial | 0.43 | 0.68 |
| Microsomal | 1.18 | 1.05 |
| "Soluble" | 0.31 | 0.29 |

[1] Adapted from Webster (1954b, 1955).

almost exclusively with calf thymus nuclei (Allfrey, 1954; Allfrey, *et al.*, 1957). Such nuclei incorporate amino acids steadily for at least two hours. The incorporation requires energy, and appears to be the result of protein synthesis rather than some exchange process. If the nuclei are fractionated after incorporation of $C^{14}$-alanine, the greatest specific activity

TABLE XIV

Distribution of $C^{14}$-Alanine in Various Protein Fractions of Nuclei[1]

| Fraction | Counts per minute per milligram |
|---|---|
| Total nuclear protein | 107. |
| I Protein extractable with pH 7.1 buffer (RNA plus protein) | 179. |
| II Protein not extractable with 1 M NaCl (RNA plus protein) | 117. |
| III Histones | 36. |
| IV Gelatinous protein | 157. |
| V Non-histone protein associated with DNA | 243. |

[1] Adapted from Allfrey, et al. (1957).

resides in a non-histone protein associated with DNA, the next greatest in a protein associated with RNA, and the least in the histone fraction (Table XIV). These results suggest that nuclei, despite their inherent complexity, may contain specific sites of protein synthesis which might be separated from the rest of the nuclear material and studied in detail. In contrast to other systems, amino acid incorporation by thymus nuclei is promoted by sodium ions and inhibited by potassium ions. Furthermore, incorporation is inhibited by deoxyribonuclease but not by ribonuclease. The ability of deoxyribonuclease-treated nuclei to incorporate amino acids into protein can be restored partly by preparations of DNA, RNA, or ribonuclease-treated RNA. It would be of great interest to know whether other isolated nuclei exhibit the same characteristics as thymus nuclei.

*Mitochondria.* Like nuclei, mitochondria in the intact cell readily incorporate amino acids into their protein (Borsook, 1953). Isolated mitochondria from both plants (Webster, 1954a) and animals (Peterson, *et al.*, 1951; McClean, *et al.*, 1956) also incorporate amino acids into protein. The incorporation is stopped by stopping oxidative phosphorylation in the mitochondria, and is promoted by a mixture of amino acids (Peterson, *et al.*, 1951). If the isolated mitochondria are washed extensively, they require the presence of the proteins not sedimented at 105,000 × g in order to have incorporation proceed (Simpson, *et al.*, 1957). Incorporation is not inhibited by ribonuclease, although the mitochondria apparently contain RNA. Like nuclei, mitochondria have the disadvantage of being relatively large and complex. However, the success of many investigators in liberating multi-enzyme systems from mitochondria suggests that a similar separation of a protein-forming system is possible.

*Chloroplasts.* Although chloroplasts, both in the cell and in an isolated state, are able to incorporate amino acids into protein (Stephenson, *et al.*, 1956; Sisakyan and Filippovich, 1957), little is known concerning the nature of the incorporation process. Its dependence upon energy, however, seems likely from the observation of Stephenson, *et al.* (1956) that chloroplasts incorporate considerably more amino acid in the light than in darkness.

*Microsomes.* Amino acid incorporation by microsomes has been investigated more extensively than incorporation by any cellular fraction, because microsomes, in intact cells, are usually far more active at incorporation than other cellular fractions (Table XIII). Isolated microsomes have a complex set of requirements for amino acid incorporation. These include: ATP (ADP and AMP are inactive), some system for regenerating ATP, magnesium and potassium ions, and the cytoplasmic protein not sedimented at 105,000 × g (Zamecnik and Keller, 1954; Hoagland, *et al.*, 1956; Sachs, 1957). Liver microsomes require, in addition, the presence of guanosine diphosphate or guanosine triphosphate (Keller and Zamecnik, 1956). Amino acid incorporation by microsomes is completely inhibited by ribonuclease.

*Ribonucleoprotein particles.* When microsomal preparations from plants or animals are examined by electron microscopy, they are found to consist of small ribonucleoprotein particles attached to protein strands. As can be seen from Figure 24, amino acids are incorporated initially into the protein of the ribonucleoprotein particles, and then into the protein strands (Littlefield, *et al.*, 1955). This suggests that ribonucleoprotein particles are the initial sites of amino acid incorporation by microsomes. Ribonucleoprotein particles have been isolated from bean seedlings (Robinson and Brown, 1953), pea seedlings (Tso, *et al.*, 1956), yeast (Chao and Schachman, 1956), Ehrlich ascites tumor cells (Littlefield and Keller, 1957), and liver microsomes (Peterman and Hamilton, 1957). The particles from Ehrlich ascites tumor cells (Littlefield and Keller, 1957), from yeast, and from pea seedlings (Webster, 1957e) possess marked abilities to incorporate a variety of amino acids into protein under roughly the same conditions as required for amino acid incorporation by microsomes. The kinetics of incorporation (Figure 25) exhibit the same rapid uptake of amino acid as is exhibited by the particles when

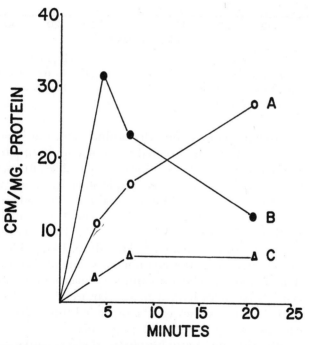

Figure 24. Incorporation of $C^{14}$-leucine into various microsomal fractions and into "soluble" cellular protein. A, deoxycholate-soluble fraction (mostly protein strands); B, deoxycholate-insoluble fraction (mostly ribonucleoprotein particles; C, "soluble" protein. Adapted from Littlefield, *et al.* (1955).

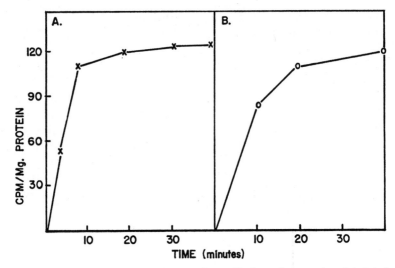

Figure 25. Incorporation of C[14]-amino acids into the protein of isolated ribonucleoprotein particles. A, C[14]-alanine incorporation by pea seedling ribonucleoprotein particles. B, C[14]-leucine incorporation by Ehrlich ascites tumor ribonucleoprotein particles.

they are in microsomes, but the amino acid, once incorporated, does not leave the isolated ribonucleoprotein particles.

The microsomal ribonucleoprotein particles investigated thus far appear to be relatively simple structures, and resemble the small plant viruses. They contain 30–50% ribonucleic acid, 50–70% protein, and possibly a small amount of uncharacterized phospholipid (Tso, *et al.*, 1956; Chao and Schachman, 1956; Peterman and Hamilton, 1957). The particles exhibit only one major component in the ultracentrifuge, and seem, therefore, to be quite uniform macromolecules. The pea seedling particles have a molecular weight of about 4.5 million. Like viruses, they can be degraded into smaller units by a variety of relatively mild procedures, including treatment with Versene, pyrophosphate, dodecyl sulfate, weak alkali (pH 10.5), acetone, and sonic vibration (Webster, 1957b,e). Such procedures, with the exception of sonic vibration, uniformly eliminate the ability of the particles to incorporate amino acids into protein. Sonic vibration, under certain conditions, results in the production of a smaller ribonucleoprotein fraction (sedimentable only after six hours at $105,000 \times g$) that is still capable of amino acid incorporation into protein in much the same manner as intact ribonucleoprotein particles (Webster, 1957b,e). Studies with ribonucleoprotein particles are still in a very early stage, but their high activity, their uniformity and relative structural simplicity, and their apparent freedom from extraneous reactions not associated with amino acid incorporation make the particles extremely useful for investigation of the mechanism of amino acid incorporation into protein.

## STUDIES ON THE MECHANISM
### OF PROTEIN SYNTHESIS

Over the years, many theories have been proposed to describe the manner in which a protein molecule is formed. The considerable increase in our knowledge of the characteristics of protein synthesis in recent years, however, has made it possible to suggest mechanisms of protein synthesis that are largely compatible with experimental data.

In all discussions of protein synthesis today, the crucial problem concerns the manner in which nucleic acid may be implicated in the synthetic process. Because of the probable function of nucleic acids as information carriers in heredity, the commonly accepted thought has been that they function in arranging amino acids in a specific sequence in the synthesis of protein. It should not be forgotten, however, that this supposition is neither supported nor repudiated by experimental evidence as yet. In an attempt to stimulate thinking and experimentation on the role of nucleic acid in protein synthesis, Dounce (1952) postulated the mechanism of protein synthesis presented in Figure 26. The important features of the mechanism are: (a) the implication of polynucleotide in determining the sequence of amino acids in protein, (b) activation of nucleic acid by the formation of triply esterified phosphate, and (c) activation of amino acids initially through their amino groups. Although Dounce and Kay (1953) found

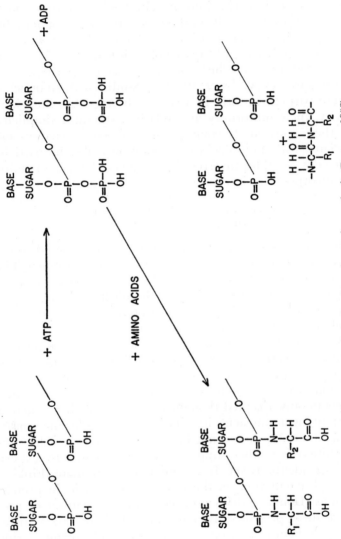

Figure 26. Suggested mechanism of protein synthesis (Dounce, 1952).

some evidence that ribonucleic acid can be phosphorylated by the ATP-myokinase system, other information on the nature of protein synthesis (carboxyl activation of amino acids, for example) is difficult to reconcile with this mechanism. An analogous proposal of Lipmann (1954), in which undefined centers on the nucleic acid molecule are activated by transfer of pyrophosphate from ATP, is similarly difficult to adapt to our knowledge of amino acid activation, as well as to other properties of protein synthesis. Borsook (1956) has eliminated this difficulty by proposing that amino acids are attached to nucleic acids by their carboxyl groups. The importance of all of these proposals, however, is that they have focused attention on: (a) the fact that amino acids must somehow be "activated" before condensing into a protein molecule, and (b) the manner in which nucleic acids might act in the formation of a particular amino acid sequence in protein.

The development of relatively simple experimental systems has made it possible to investigate the mechanism of protein synthesis. Although the studies are only beginning, the results obtained indicate that protein synthesis can be divided operationally into several distinct phases. These are: (a) the activation of amino acids through the intermediate formation of enzyme-bound amino acid-AMP compounds, (b) transfer of the amino acid to some polynucleotide or nucleotide-containing acceptor, (c) positioning of the amino acids in a specific sequence by the "protein-forming system" (probably a nucleoprotein), (d) formation of the peptide bonds of the protein, and (e) liberation of the protein from the protein-forming system.

*Amino acid activation.* A study of the manner of formation of simple peptidic substances (Chapter 3) has shown that the activation of amino acids prior to the synthesis of peptidic linkages proceeds in either of two ways:

$$E + \text{amino acid} + ATP \rightleftharpoons E - \text{amino acid phosphate} + ADP \quad (a)$$

$$E + \text{amino acid} + ATP \rightleftharpoons$$
$$E - \text{amino acid} - AMP + \text{pyrophosphate} \quad (b)$$

These results led to the idea that the first step in protein synthesis might also be an interaction between amino acids and ATP. As the above reactions are reversible, amino acid activation should be detectable by the presence of an amino acid-dependent exchange of either ADP or pyrophosphate with ATP. Using this approach, Hoagland (1955) found an amino acid-dependent exchange of $P^{32}$-pyrophosphate with ATP catalyzed by an enzyme preparation from rat liver. Significantly, this preparation is essential for the incorporation of amino acids into microsomal or mitochondrial protein (Hoagland, *et al.*, 1956; Simpson, *et al.*, 1957). A similar exchange reaction has been found in bacteria, yeast, and *Neurospora* (DeMoss and Novelli, 1955, 1956; Novelli and DeMoss, 1958), as well as in various higher plants (Davis, *et al.*, 1957; Webster, 1957e; Clark, 1957). The enzyme preparations also catalyze the synthesis of amino acid hydroxamates according to the reaction:

Amino acid + Hydroxylamine + ATP $\longrightarrow$

Amino acid hydroxamate + AMP + pyrophosphate

In addition, the preparations catalyze the synthesis of ATP from pyrophosphate and synthetic amino acid-AMP compounds (DeMoss, *et al.*, 1956; Berg, 1957). These facts, plus the lack of formation of detectable quantities of free amino acid-AMP compounds has led to the postulation of an enzyme-bound amino acid-AMP compound (Figure 27) as an intermediate in amino acid activation. Further evidence in support of this has been obtained by the finding that the carboxyl oxygen of oxygen-18-labeled amino acids is transferred to the liberated AMP during the synthesis of amino acid hydroxamates by amino acid activating enzyme preparations (Hoagland, *et al.*, 1957; Bernlohr and Webster, 1958).

Although, at a given pH, the amino acids generally found in protein do not always exhibit the amino acid-dependent pyrophosphate-ATP exchange, they do exhibit hydroxamate formation (Table XV). Some preparations exhibit pyrophosphate-ATP exchange with every amino acid (Nisman, *et al.*,

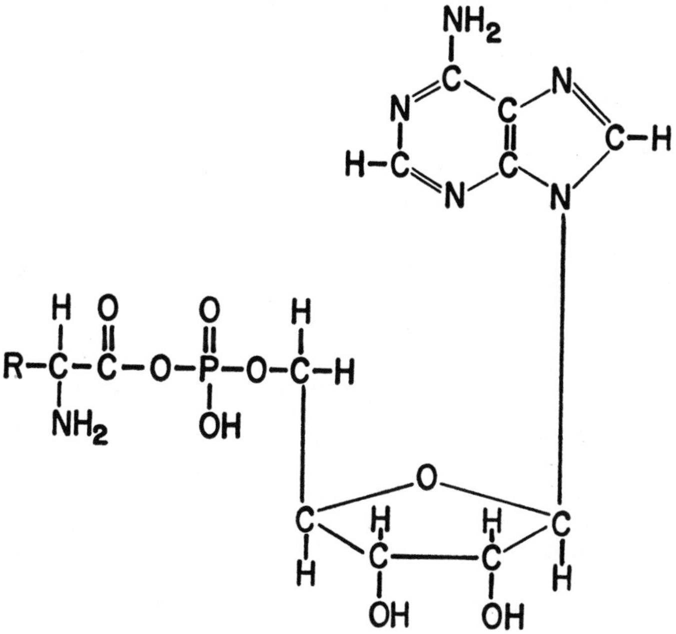

Figure 27. Amino acid-AMP compound.

1957; Lipmann, 1958), while others exhibit such exchange with most (Clark, 1957) or all (Webster, 1958) amino acids only when the pH optimum for each amino acid is used. There is evidence, therefore, for the activation of all amino acids normally found in protein. Available evidence supports the view that the different amino acids are activated by separate activating enzymes. The tryptophan activating enzyme has been purified considerably (Davie, *et al.*, 1956), and several other activating enzymes have been purified partially from various sources (Table XVI).

The formation of enzyme-bound amino acid-AMP compounds undoubtedly represents only the first step in amino acid activation. By analogy with other reactions involving the formation of acyl-AMP intermediates, the amino acid would be expected to be transferred to some acceptor.

## TABLE XV
Amino Acid Hydroxamate Formation by Amino
Acid Activation Enzyme Preparations

| Amino acid | Activation enzyme preparation | | |
|---|---|---|---|
| | E. coli[1] ($\mu$M/ml.) | yeast[2] ($\mu$M/5 mg. protein) | pea seedlings[3] ($\mu$M/5 mg. protein) |
| Alanine | 0.40 | 0.05 | 1.05 |
| Arginine | 0.95 | 0.10 | 0.50 |
| Glycine | 0.40 | 0.0 | 0.40 |
| Histidine | 0.10 | 0.20 | 0.55 |
| Hydroxyproline | 0.20 | — | — |
| Isoleucine | 0.15 | 0.05 | 1.00 |
| Leucine | 0.15 | 0.15 | 0.30 |
| Lysine | 0.0 | 0.0 | 0.50 |
| Methionine | 1.05 | 0.15 | 1.10 |
| Phenylalanine | 1.50 | 0.20 | 0.50 |
| Proline | 0.15 | — | 0.05 |
| Serine | 0.55 | 0.05 | 0.10 |
| Threonine | 0.65 | 0.05 | 0.30 |
| Tryptophan | 1.25 | 0.30 | 1.15 |
| Tyrosine | 3.35 | 0.75 | 0.30 |
| Valine | 0.0 | 0.10 | 0.90 |

[1] Novelli and DeMoss (1958).

[2] Webster, unpublished experiments.

[3] Webster (1957e).

## TABLE XVI
Purification of Various Amino Acid Activating Enzymes

| Enzyme | Source | State of purity | Reference |
|---|---|---|---|
| Alanine-activating | Hog liver | 15-fold purified | Bernlohr and Webster (1958). |
| Leucine-activating | E. coli | 20-fold " | DeMoss and Novelli (1956). |
| Methionine-activating | Yeast | 45-fold " | Berg (1956). |
| Tryptophan-activating | Beef pancreas | 215-fold " (70–80% pure) | Davie, et al. (1956). |
| Tyrosine-activating | Yeast | 50-fold purified | Koningsberger, et al. (1957). |
| Valine-activating | Pea seeds | 8-fold " | Webster (unpublished). |

E + amino acid + ATP $\rightleftharpoons$

E — amino acid — AMP + pyrophosphate

E — amino acid — AMP + X $\rightleftharpoons$ E + amino acid — X + AMP

This second reaction might be detected as an amino acid-dependent exchange of AMP with ATP. Such a reaction was first observed by Holley (1957), using an activating enzyme preparation from rat liver, and later by Webster (1957b), with an enzyme preparation from pea seedlings. Both investigators found the reaction to be inhibited by ribonuclease, suggesting that the acceptor might contain a polynucleotide. Webster (1957b) further observed that an amino acid incorporation system from pea seedlings can be separated into three fractions. These are: (a) a fraction containing amino acid-activating enzymes, (b) a fraction with no activity alone, but which allows an amino acid-dependent AMP-ATP exchange when combined with the activating enzymes, and (c) a nucleoprotein fraction which incorporates amino acids into protein, if both other fractions are present. These results are compatible with the formation of an amino acid-X compound as a prerequisite to the incorporation of amino acid into protein. Hoagland, *et al.* (1957) have found that the rat liver amino acid activating enzyme preparation contains a small quantity of polynucleotide. When the preparation is incubated with ATP and a labeled amino acid, the amino acid is bound to the polynucleotide material by a linkage that is stable in dilute trichloroacetic acid, but is hydrolyzed in dilute alkali. If the polynucleotide, after reaction with ATP and amino acid, is incubated with hydroxylamine, amino acid hydroxamate is formed. Most importantly, if the polynucleotide containing the bound amino acid is incubated with microsomes in the absence of activating enzymes, the amino acid is incorporated into microsomal protein. All of these findings indicate that an amino acid, after initial reaction with ATP to form enzyme-bound amino acid-AMP, is transferred to some unknown material, possibly a polynucleotide, to form an amino acid-X compound. The protein-forming system of nucleoprotein particles is then able to catalyze peptide bond formation between amino acids that have been activated through the formation of amino acid-X compounds. Therefore, a primary problem in the further elucidation of the mechanism of protein synthesis involves not only the purification and characterization of amino acid activating enzymes, but also the identification of the factors which may accept the amino acid from AMP. Fortunately, both aspects of the problem appear to be approachable by standard biochemical methods.

*Peptide bond synthesis.* Although the manner in which amino acids are initially activated is steadily becoming clearer, the manner in which activated amino acids are condensed together to form proteins is still not understood. Studies on the synthesis of simple peptides (Chapter 3) have shown that enzyme-catalyzed peptide bond formation between two amino acids proceeds readily following the activation of one of the amino acids by reaction with ATP. It seems possible, therefore, that the protein portion of microsomal or other nucleoprotein particles is capable of catalyzing peptide bond synthesis between activated amino acids. It also seems possible that the nucleic acid portion of the nucleoprotein, by interaction with the factor attached to an activated amino acid, acts to specify the order in which different activated amino acids can approach the site of peptide bond synthesis. In this manner the amino acids would be condensed successively in the sequence of a particular protein, as specified by the nucleic acid (Figure 28). This is probably the simplest mechanism compatible with existing experimental results.

The problem of cellular protein synthesis may actually be two problems: (a) the synthesis of various proteins through the action of nucleoprotein "templates," and (b) the replication of the nucleoprotein itself. These processes could well proceed differently beyond the amino acid activation stage. In the case of nucleoprotein replication, the synthesis of both protein and nucleic acid is involved. Thus, it is not surprising that much experimental evidence exists suggesting some kind of linkage between protein and nucleic acid syntheses (Gale, 1953, 1954; Pardee, 1954; Spiegelman, *et al.*, 1954; Hal-

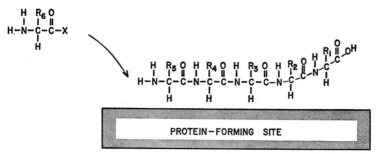

Figure 28. Condensation of activated amino acids on a nucleoprotein template.

verson and Jackson, 1956; Creaser, 1955; Pardee and Prestidge, 1956; Spiegelman, 1957; Webster and Johnson, 1955; Webster, 1957a,d). However, the synthesis of nucleic acid could proceed either separately from protein synthesis or as part of the mechanism of protein synthesis. In the first case (Figure 29), a specific polynucleotide might be formed initially (possibly in the nucleus). Such a polynucleotide would then become associated with amino acids, either before or after binding to an existing nucleoprotein. The amino acids could then be condensed with the resultant production of a new nucleoprotein molecule. As nucleoprotein particles appear to contain protein subunits, it would also be possible for the protein subunits to be produced as shown in Figure 28, and then assembled in association with a polynucleotide in the manner already demonstrated with tobacco mosaic virus.

The simultaneous and interdependent synthesis of protein and nucleic acid is difficult to envision. However, it might occur if amino acid activation resulted in the eventual formation of nucleotide diphospho-amino acids. Under these circumstances, various nucleoside diphospho-amino acids could bind, in specific sequence, on a nucleoprotein template (Figure 30). Cleavage of the bond between the terminal phosphate and the amino acid would result in the formation of peptide bonds between adjacent amino acids, while subsequent cleavage of the pyrophosphate bond of the nucleoside diphosphate would result in the formation of a specific poly-

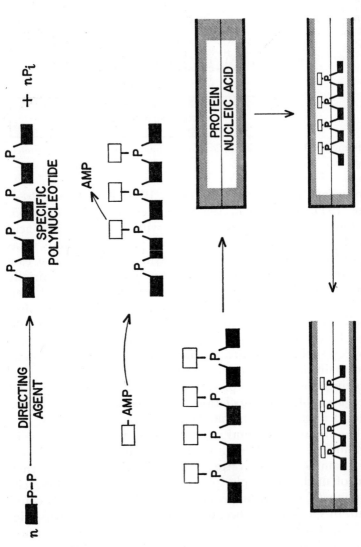

Figure 29. Separate formation of protein and nucleic acid. Open squares, amino acid; solid squares, nucleoside.

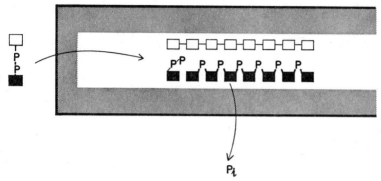

Figure 30. Simultaneous formation of protein and nucleic acid from nucleoside diphospho-amino acids. Open squares, amino acid; solid squares, nucleoside.

nucleotide (Webster, 1957c). Evidence for the formation of mononucleotide-amino acid compounds as a result of amino acid activation has not been obtained, however. Instead, the amino acids appear to bind to some form of polynucleotide (Hoagland, *et al.*, 1957; Holley, 1957; Webster, 1957b). However, the possibility has not been ruled out that more than one kind of amino acid activation exists, resulting in different kinds of activated intermediates. At present, the most promising area for advancement in our knowledge of the mechanism of protein synthesis is in the further study of the formation of activated amino acids. As soon as the structure of each activated amino acid is known, it should be possible to synthesize the activated amino acid. In this manner, the complex of activating enzymes and ATP can be replaced by a mixture of activated amino acids prepared by chemical synthesis, and studies on the manner in which these precursors condense to form specific proteins can proceed with confidence. One of the mechanisms depicted above may reflect the broad outlines of the manner in which at least some proteins are formed, but it is undoubtedly incorrect in detail. It will be of great interest to learn the actual manner in which amino acids are condensed to form specific proteins.

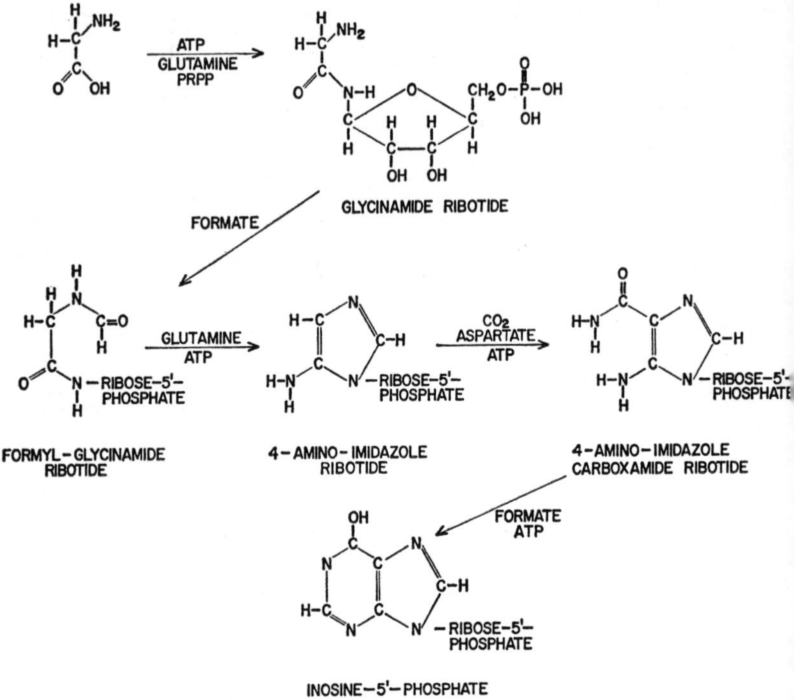

Figure 31. Biosynthesis of inosine-5′-phosphate.

## NUCLEIC ACID SYNTHESIS

Although it has been known for several years that phosphate, glycine, formate, carbon dioxide, and ammonia are efficient precursors of nucleic acid, the manner in which they combined together was not evident. It has now been shown (Goldthwaite, *et al.*, 1955a,b; Buchanan, *et al.*, 1955) that glycine, formate, carbon dioxide, ammonia, and phosphoribose pyrophosphate (PRPP) combine together to form inosine-5′-phosphate. The steps in this process are outlined in Figure 31. The further transformation of inosine-5′-phosphate into adenosine-5′-phosphate has been found to proceed as follows (Carter and Cohen, 1955; Lieberman, 1956):

Inosine-5′-phosphate + aspartate ⇌ Adenylosuccinate

Adenylosuccinate ⇌ adenosine-5′-phosphate + fumarate

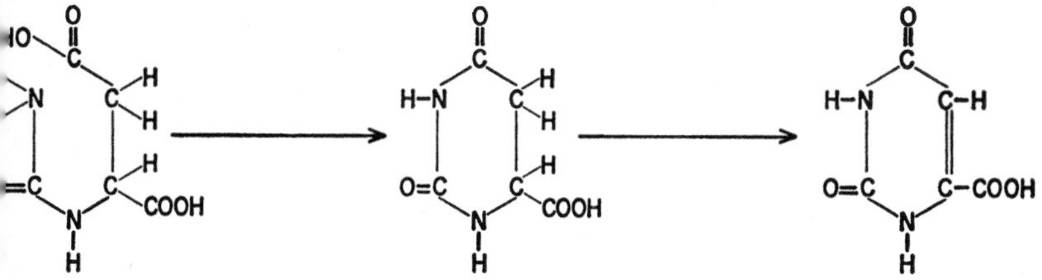

CARBAMYL—
ASPARTATE                    DIHYDRO—OROTIC                    OROTIC ACID
                                  ACID

Figure 32. Conversion of carbamyl aspartate to orotic acid.

Likewise, the biosynthesis of pyrimidine nucleotides has been clarified. The first step in the synthesis of both pyrimidine nucleotides of ribonucleic acid is the condensation of carbon dioxide, ammonia, and aspartate (probably through the intermediate formation of carbamyl phosphate) to form carbamyl aspartate (Jones, *et al.*, 1955):

$$CO_2 + NH_3 + ATP \longrightarrow \text{Carbamyl phosphate} + ADP$$

carbamyl phosphate + aspartate $\longrightarrow$

carbamyl aspartate + phosphate

Carbamyl aspartate is then cyclized as shown in Figure 32 to form orotic acid. The outstanding work of Lieberman and Kornberg (1954) has shown that orotic acid is transformed into orotidine-5′-phosphate and thence into uridine and cytidine phosphates by the following reactions:

orotic acid + phosphoribose pyrophosphate $\longrightarrow$

orotidine-5′-phosphate + pyrophosphate

orotidine-5′-phosphate $\longrightarrow$ uridine-5′-phosphate + $CO_2$

uridine-5′-phosphate + ATP $\longrightarrow$ uridine-5′-diphosphate + ADP

2 uridine-5′-diphosphate $\longrightarrow$

uridine-5′-triphosphate + uridine-5′-phosphate

uridine-5′-triphosphate + $NH_3$ + ATP $\longrightarrow$

cytidine-5′-triphosphate + ADP + orthophosphate

It is interesting that the uridine nucleotide must be in the form of a triphosphate in order to be transformed into a cytidine nucleotide.

Considerable evidence now implicates the four ribonucleotides discussed above as intermediates in the biosynthesis of ribonucleic acid. The manner in which these nucleotides are converted into specific nucleic acids is not clear. A signal contribution to our understanding of ribonucleic acid synthesis, however, has been made by Grunberg-Manago, *et al.* (1955, 1956) who have found an enzyme, polynucleotide phosphorylase, in bacteria, fungi, and higher plants which catalyzes a reversible phosphorolysis of ribonucleic acid.

n nucleoside-5′-diphosphate $\rightleftharpoons$

ribonucleic acid + n orthophosphate

The nature of the ribonucleic acid formed by the isolated enzyme depends upon the nucleoside-5′-diphosphates present. Thus, a means is available, through the activity of polynucleotide phosphorylase, for the biosynthesis of ribonucleic acid from nucleotides. Whether the enzyme mediates normal ribonucleic acid synthesis, and whether it constitutes the only mechanism for cellular ribonucleic acid synthesis is not yet known. If it does participate in normal RNA synthesis, however, it presumably operates under some directing force which allows the formation of specific nucleic acids. In this connection, the necessity for catalytic amounts of the deficient amino acid for RNA synthesis by amino acid-requiring bacteria (Pardee and Prestidge, 1956) is perhaps significant, and suggests the participation of free amino acids or protein synthesis in RNA synthesis.

An impressive beginning has also been made on the elucidation of the manner of synthesis of deoxyribonucleic acid (DNA). Although the manner of synthesis of deoxyribonucleotides is not clear, Kornberg and coworkers (1957) have purified greatly an enzyme from *E. coli* which catalyzes the synthesis of DNA from a mixture of the four deoxyribonucleotides found in DNA, according to the following reaction:

$$\text{n Deoxyribonucleoside-5'-triphosphates} \xrightarrow{\text{DNA, Mg}^{++}}$$

$$\text{DNA} + \text{n pyrophosphate}$$

Unlike ribonucleic acid synthesis, which requires nucleoside diphosphates, the nucleoside triphosphates are specifically required here. The reaction requires the presence of all four nucleotides simultaneously, as well as a small amount of DNA "primer." Whether the primer acts to specify the sequence of nucleotides in the newly formed DNA is not yet known. In view of the potential importance of both DNA and RNA as information carriers, knowledge of their synthesis is highly important. Further details on these syntheses and their participation in cellular DNA and RNA formation are greatly needed.

## PROTEIN DEGRADATION

In contrast to the vast amount of work on protein synthesis, the effort expended on finding out how proteins break down in living cells is very small. The occurrence of various peptidases and proteases in plants has been chronicled in many reviews on proteolytic enzymes and will not be repeated here. There are two obvious ways in which proteins could be broken down in living cells: (a) by proteolytic enzymes, and (b) by a reversal of protein synthesis. There is no *a priori* reason to suppose that proteolytic enzymes function as agents for protein breakdown in living cells, and their role in this process remains to be established. A more useful method of breakdown (from the standpoint of cellular economy) would be via a reversal of synthesis, in which the breakdown should be accompanied by the synthesis of considerable quantities of ATP. Although this method seems unlikely at first glance, it is very similar to the synthesis of ATP during the breakdown of the amide, glutamine, or the dipeptide, glutamylcysteine.

$$\text{glutamine} + \text{ADP} + \text{P}_i \longrightarrow \text{glutamate} + \text{NH}_3 + \text{ATP}$$

$$\text{glutamylcysteine} + \text{ADP} + \text{P}_i \longrightarrow$$

$$\text{glutamate} + \text{cysteine} + \text{ATP}$$

$$\text{protein} + (\text{AMP} + \text{P} - \text{P}_i) \longrightarrow \text{amino acids} + \text{ATP}$$

Such a process could serve as an important energy source for the cell under certain conditions. As the equilibrium in protein synthesis is apparently similar to that in amide or peptide synthesis, the possibility of some protein being broken down this way must be considered.

The suggestion that protein degradation requires energy has arisen from the observations of both Simpson (1953) and Steinberg, *et al.* (1956) that protein degradation in mammalian cells is inhibited by respiratory inhibitors and dinitrophenol. Similarly, inhibitors of protein synthesis, such as parafluorophenylalanine, inhibit protein breakdown in living cells, but neither these nor respiratory inhibitors have any effect on autolytic protein breakdown in disrupted cells. Therefore, Steinberg, *et al.* (1956) question the participation of the well-known proteolytic enzymes in normal cellular protein breakdown. They point out that reversibility for one or more stages of protein synthesis would be compatible with their findings. These results are extremely important, and it would appear that the cellular breakdown of protein may offer as fertile a field for investigation as protein synthesis. In fact if protein breakdown does proceed by a reversal of protein synthesis, then the study of protein breakdown provides us with a means for studying the last step in protein synthesis, the interaction of the protein-forming system with its product, protein.

*Summary.* The overall picture in the study of protein and nucleic acid metabolism is very bright. Our rapidly increasing knowledge of the factors necessary for protein synthesis, the nature of the organized cellular components that form protein, and the exciting beginnings of the characterization of amino acid activation, all promise that giant strides will be made in the next few years in understanding the chemical pathways involved in protein synthesis.

## REFERENCES

ABRAMS, R. AND BENTLEY, M., Arch. Biochem. Biophys. **58,** 109 (1955).
ALLFREY, V., Proc. Natl. Acad. Sci. **40,** 881 (1954).
ALLFREY, V., MIRSKY, A. E., AND OSAWA, S., in *Chemical Basis of Heredity* (McElroy, W. D. and Glass, B., Eds.), Johns Hopkins Press, Baltimore (1957).

BAKER, R. S., JOHNSON, J. E., AND FOX, S., Federation Proc. 13, 178 (1954).

BARON, L. S., SPIEGELMAN, S., AND QUASTLER, H. J., Jour. Gen. Physiol. 36, 631 (1953).

BENDICH, A., FRESCO, J. R., ROSENKRANTZ, H. S., AND BEISER, S. M., Jour. Am. Chem. Soc. 77, 3671 (1955).

BERG, P., Jour. Biol. Chem. 222, 1025 (1956).

BERG, P., Federation Proc. 16, 152 (1957).

BERNLOHR, R. W. AND WEBSTER, G. C., Arch. Biochem. Biophys. 73, 276 (1958).

BORSOOK, H., Adv. in Protein Chem. 8, 127 (1953).

BORSOOK, H., Jour. Cell. Comp. Physiol. 47 (Supplement 1), 35 (1956).

BORSOOK, H., DEASY, C. L., HAAGEN-SMIT, A. J., KEIGHLEY, G., AND LOWY, P. H., Jour. Biol. Chem. 187, 839 (1950).

BRACHET, J., Chemical Embryology, Interscience Press, New York (1952).

BRACHET, J., Nature 174, 876 (1954).

BREITMAN, T. R. AND WEBSTER, G. C., Biochim. Biophys. Acta 27, 408 (1958).

BUCHANAN, J. M., LEVENBERG, B., FLAKS, J. G., AND GLADNER, J. A., in Amino Acid Metabolism (McElroy, W. D. and Glass, B., Eds.), Johns Hopkins Press, Baltimore (1955).

BURMA, D. P. AND BURRIS, R. H., Jour. Biol. Chem. 225, 723 (1957).

CANELLAKIS, E. S., Biochim. Biophys. Acta 23, 217 (1957).

CARTER, C. E. AND COHEN, L. H., Jour. Am. Chem. Soc. 77, 499 (1955).

CASPERSSON, T. O., Symp. Soc. Exptl. Biol. 1, 127 (1947).

CHANTRENNE, H., Nature 177, 579 (1956).

CHAO, F. AND SCHACHMAN, H. K., Arch. Biochem. Biophys. 61, 220 (1956).

CHRISTIANSEN, H. N., in Amino Acid Metabolism (McElroy, W. D., and Glass, B., Eds.), Johns Hopkins Press, Baltimore (1955).

CLARK, J. M., JR., Plant Physiol. 32 (Supplement), XXXV (1957).

COHEN, G. N. AND COWIE, D. B., Compt. rend. 244, 680 (1957).

COHEN, S. AND BARNER, H. D., Federation Proc. 13, 193 (1954).

CORNWELL, D. AND LUCK, J. M., Arch. Biochem. Biophys. (in press) (1958).

CREASER, E. H., Nature 175, 899 (1955).

CROOK, E. M. (Editor), The Structure of Nucleic Acids and Their Role in Protein Synthesis, Cambridge Univ. Press, Cambridge (1957).

DAVIE, E. W., KONINGSBERGER, V. V., AND LIPMANN, F., Arch. Biochem. Biophys. 65, 21 (1956).

DAVÍS, J. W., BEST, A. N., AND NOVELLI, G. D., Federation Proc. 16, 170 (1957).

DEMOSS, J. A. AND NOVELLI, G. D., Biochim. Biophys. Acta 18, 592 (1955).

DEMOSS, J. A. AND NOVELLI, G. D., Biochim. Biophys. Acta 22, 49 (1956).

DEMOSS, J. A., GENUTH, S. M., AND NOVELLI, G. D., Proc. Natl. Acad. Sci. 42, 325 (1956).

DITTMER, K., Abstracts, Amer. Chem. Soc. 36c(1957).

DOUNCE, A. L., Enzymologia 15, 251 (1952).

DOUNCE, A. L. AND KAY, E. R. M., Proc. Soc. Exptl. Biol. Med. 83, 321 (1953).

FRAZIER, L. E., WISSLER, R. W., STEFFEE, C. H., WOOLRIDGE, R. L., AND CANNON, P. R., Jour. Nutrition 33, 65 (1947).

GALE, E. F., Adv. in Protein Chem. 8, 285 (1953).

GALE, E. F., in Amino Acid Metabolism (McElroy, W. D., and Glass, B., Eds.), Johns Hopkins Press, Baltimore (1955).

GALE, E. F., Biochem. Jour. 62, 40P (1956).

GALE, E. F. AND FOLKES, J. P., Biochem. Jour. 53, 483 (1953a).

GALE, E. F. AND FOLKES, J. P., Biochem. Jour. 53, 493 (1953b).

GALE, E. F. AND FOLKES, J. P., Biochem. Jour. 59, 675 (1955a).

GALE, E. F. AND FOLKES, J. P., Biochem. Jour. **59**, 661 (1955b).
GALE, E. F. AND FOLKES, J. P., Nature **175**, 592 (1955c).
GEHRIG, L. B. AND MAGASANIK, B., Jour. Am. Chem. Soc. **77**, 4685 (1955).
GEIGER, E., Jour. Nutrition **34**, 97 (1947).
GEIGER, E., Science **111**, 594 (1950).
GOLDTHWAITE, D. A., PEABODY, R. A., AND GREENBERG, G. R., in *Amino Acid Metabolism* (McElroy, W. D., and Glass, B., Eds.), Johns Hopkins Press, Baltimore (1955a).
GOLDTHWAITE, D. A., GREENBERG, G. R., AND PEABODY, R. A., Biochim. Biophys. Acta **18**, 148 (1955b).
GOLDWASSER, E., Jour. Am. Chem. Soc. **77**, 6083 (1955).
GREEN, H. AND ANKER, H. S., Biochim. Biophys. Acta **13**, 365 (1954).
GROSS, D. AND TARVER, H., Jour. Biol. Chem. **217**, 169 (1955).
GROTH, D. P., Biochim. Biophys. Acta **21**, 18 (1956).
GRUNBERG-MANAGO, M., ORTIZ, P. J., AND OCHOA, S., Science **122**, 907 (1955).
GRUNBERG-MANAGO, M., ORTIZ, P., AND OCHOA, S., Biochim. Biophys. Acta **20**, 269 (1956).
HALVORSON, H. AND JACKSON, L., Jour. Gen. Microbiol. **14**, 26 (1956).
HALVORSON, H. O. AND SPIEGELMAN, S., Jour. Bacteriol. **64**, 207 (1952).
HALVORSON, H. O. AND SPIEGELMAN, S., Jour. Bacteriol. **65**, 496 (1953).
HALVORSON, H. O., SPIEGELMAN, S., AND HINMAN, R., Arch. Biochem. Biophys. **55**, 512 (1955).
HEIDELBERGER, C., HARBERS, E., LEIBMAN, K., TAKAGI, Y., AND POTTER, V. R., Biochim. Biophys. Acta **20**, 445 (1956).
HEINRICH, M. R., DEWEY, V. C., PARKS, R. E., JR., AND KIDDER, G. W., Jour. Biol. Chem. **197**, 199 (1952).
HOAGLAND, M. B., Biochim. Biophys. Acta **16**, 288 (1955).
HOAGLAND, M. B., KELLER, E. B., AND ZAMECNIK, P. C., Jour. Biol. Chem. **218**, 345 (1956).
HOAGLAND, M. B., ZAMECNIK, P. C., AND STEPHENSON, M. L., Biochim. Biophys. Acta **24**, 215 (1957).
HOAGLAND, M. B., ZAMECNIK, P. C., SHARON, N., LIPMANN, F., STULBERG, M. P., AND BOYER, P. D., Biochim. Biophys. Acta **26**, 215 (1957).
HOLLY, R. W., Jour. Am. Chem. Soc. **79**, 658 (1957).
JONES, M. E., SPECTOR, L., AND LIPMANN, F., Jour. Am. Chem. Soc. **77**, 819 (1955).
KAUFMANN, B. P. AND DAS, N. K., Carnegie Inst. of Washington Year Book 52, 238 (1953).
KELLER, E. B. AND ZAMECNIK, P. C., Jour. Biol. Chem. **221**, 45 (1956).
KELNER, A., Jour. Bacteriol. **65**, 252 (1953).
KONINGSBERGER, V. V., VAN DE VEN, A. M., AND OVERBEEK, J. T. G., Kon. Akad. Wetenschap., Proc. **B60**, 141 (1957).
KORNBERG, A., in *Chemical Basis of Heredity* (McElroy, W. D., and Glass, B., Eds.), Johns Hopkins Press, Baltimore (1957).
LAGERKVIST, U., Acta Chem. Scand. **9**, 1028 (1955).
LANDMAN, O. E. AND SPIEGELMAN, S., Proc. Natl. Acad. Sci. **41**, 698 (1955).
LASNITZKI, I., MATTHEWS, R. E. F., AND SMITH, J. D., Nature **173**, 346 (1954).
LEE, N. D. AND WILLIAMS, R. H., Biochim. Biophys. Acta **9**, 698 (1952).
LEPAGE, G., Proc. Soc. Exptl. Biol. Med. **83**, 724 (1953).
LESTER, R. L., Jour. Am. Chem. Soc. **75**, 5448 (1953).
LESTER, R. L., Incorporation of Amino Acids into the Proteins of *Micrococcus lysodeikticus*. Ph.D. Thesis, Calif. Inst. of Technology, Pasadena, 1955.

LEVY, H. B., SKUTCH, E. T., AND SCHADE, A. L., Arch. Biochem. 24, 198 (1949).

LIEBERMAN, I., Jour. Am. Chem. Soc. 78, 251 (1956).

LIEBERMAN, I. AND KORNBERG, A., Jour. Biol. Chem. 207, 911 (1954).

LIPMANN, F., in *The Mechanism of Enzyme Action* (McElroy, W. D., and Glass, B., Eds.), Johns Hopkins Press, Baltimore (1954).

LIPMANN, F., Proc. Natl. Acad. Sci. 44, 67 (1958).

LITTLEFIELD, J. W., KELLER, E. B., GROSS, J., AND ZAMECNIK, P. C., Jour. Biol. Chem. 217, 111, (1955).

LITTLEFIELD, J. W. AND KELLER, E. B., Jour. Biol. Chem. 224, 13 (1957).

LOFTFIELD, R. B. AND HARRIS, A., Jour. Biol. Chem. 219, 151 (1956).

LOOMIS, W. F. AND LIPMANN, F., Jour. Biol. Chem. 173, 807 (1948).

MATTHEWS, R. E. F., Jour. Gen. Microbiol. 10, 521 (1954).

MATTHEWS, R. E. F. AND SMITH, J. D., Nature 177, 271 (1956).

MCLEAN, J. R., COHEN, G. L., AND SIMPSON, M. V., Federation Proc. 15, 312 (1956).

MITCHELL, J. H., JR., SKIPPER, H. E., AND BENNETT, L. L., JR., Cancer Research 10, 647 (1950).

MONOD, J., PAPPENHEIMER, A. M., JR., AND COHEN-BAZIRE, G., Biochim. Biophys. Acta 7, 648 (1952).

NISMAN, B., BERGMANN, F. H., AND BERG, P., Biochim. Biophys. Acta 26, 639 (1957).

NOVELLI, G. D. AND DEMOSS, J. A., Jour. Cell. Comp. Physiol. 49, Supplement 1 (1958).

OOTA, Y. AND OSAWA, S., Biochim. Biophys. Acta 15, 163 (1954).

PARDEE, A. B., Proc. Natl. Acad. Sci. 40, 263 (1954).

PARDEE, A. B. AND PRESTIDGE, L. S., Jour. Bacteriol. 71, 677 (1956).

PARDEE, A. B., SHORE, V. G., AND PRESTIDGE, L. S., Biochim. Biophys. Acta 21, 406 (1956).

PETERMAN, M. L. AND HAMILTON, M. G., Jour. Biol. Chem. 224, 725 (1957).

PETERSON, E. A., WINNICK, T., AND GREENBERG, D. M., Jour. Am. Chem. Soc. 73, 503 (1951).

POTTER, V. R., HECHT, L. E., AND HERBERT, E., Biochim. Biophys. Acta 20, 439 (1956).

RICKENBERG, H. V., YANOFSKY, C., AND BONNER, D. M., Jour. Bacteriol. 66, 683 (1953).

ROBINSON, E. AND BROWN, R., Nature 171, 313 (1953).

ROTMAN, B. AND SPIEGELMAN, S., Jour. Bacteriol. 68, 419 (1954).

SACHS, H., Jour. Biol. Chem. 228, 23 (1957).

SHER, H. E. AND MALETTE, M. F., Arch. Biochem. Biophys. 52, 331 (1954).

SIMKIN, J. L. AND WORK, T. S., Nature 179, 1214 (1957).

SIMPSON, M. V., Jour. Biol. Chem. 201, 143 (1953).

SIMPSON, M. V., MCLEAN, J. R., COHEN, G., AND BRANDT, I., Federation Proc. 16, 249 (1957).

SISSAKIAN, N. M. AND FILIPPOVICH, I. I., Biokhimiya 22, 375 (1957).

SNOKE, J. E., YANARI, S., AND BLOCH, K., Jour. Biol. Chem. 201, 573 (1953).

SPIEGELMAN, S., in *Chemical Basis of Heredity* (McElroy, W. D. and Glass, B., Eds.), Johns Hopkins Press, Baltimore (1957).

SPIEGELMAN, S., REINER, J. M., AND COHNBERG, R., Jour. Gen. Physiol. 31, 27 (1947).

SPIEGELMAN, S., HALVORSON, H. O., AND BEN-ISHAI, R., in *Amino Acid Metabolism* (McElroy, W. D. and Glass, B., Eds.), Johns Hopkins Press, Baltimore (1955).

STEINBERG, D., VAUGHAN, M., AND ANFINSEN, C. B., Science **124,** 389 (1956).
STEPHENSON, M. L., THIMANN, K. V., AND ZAMECNIK, P. C., Arch. Biochem. Biophys. **65,** 194 (1956).
STEWARD, F. C. AND PRESTON, C., Plant Physiol. **16,** 85 (1941).
STEWARD, F. C., BIDWELL, R. S. G., AND YEMM, E. W., Nature **178,** 734 (1956).
TARVER, H., in *The Proteins,* IIB (Neurath, H. and Bailey, K., Eds.), Academic Press, New York (1954).
TARVER, H., Federation Proc. **14,** 291 (1955).
TSO, P., BONNER, J., AND VINOGRAD, J., Jour. Biophys. Biochem. Cytology **2,** 451 (1956).
USHIBA, D. AND MAGASANIK, B., Proc. Soc. Exptl. Biol. Med. **80,** 626 (1952).
WEBSTER, G. C., Plant Physiol. **29,** 202 (1954a).
WEBSTER, G. C., Plant Physiol. **29,** 382 (1954b).
WEBSTER, G. C., Plant Physiol. **30,** 351 (1955).
WEBSTER, G. C., Biochim. Biophys. Acta **20,** 565 (1956).
WEBSTER, G. C., Arch. Biochem. Biophys. **68,** 403 (1957a).
WEBSTER, G. C., Arch. Biochem. Biophys. **70,** 622 (1957b).
WEBSTER, G. C., Acta Histochemica. **4,** 9 (1957c).
WEBSTER, G. C., in *Chemical Basis of Heredity* (McElroy, W. D. and Glass, B., Eds.), Johns Hopkins Press, Baltimore (1957d).
WEBSTER, G. C., Jour. Biol. Chem. **229,** 535 (1957e).
WEBSTER, G. C., Symposium. Soc. Exptl. Biol. (in press) (1958).
WEBSTER, G. C. AND JOHNSON, M. P., Jour. Biol. Chem. **217,** 641 (1955).
WEBSTER, G. C. AND VARNER, J. E., Arch. Biochem. Biophys. **52,** 22 (1954).
WISSEMAN, C. L., JR., SMADEL, J. E., HAHN, F. E., AND HOPPS, H. E., Jour. Bacteriol. **67,** 622 (1954).
ZAMECNIK, P. C. AND KELLER, E. B., Jour. Biol. Chem. **209,** 337 (1954).

# Chapter 5

# Nitrogen Metabolism
## in the Intact Plant

### NITROGEN METABOLISM
### IN DEVELOPING SEEDLINGS

The germination of a seed and the subsequent growth of the resulting seedling produce marked changes in the nitrogenous constituents of the seed. The most prominent of these are: (a) the breakdown of seed protein and nucleic acid, (b) the appearance of free amino acids and amino acid amides, and (c) the synthesis of new protein and nucleic acid in the growing seedling.

*Breakdown of seed protein.* It has long been known that the germination of a seed results in a steady decrease in the protein content of the seed itself, and a concomitant increase in free amino acids and amides (Chibnall, 1939). Figure 33 illustrates a typical example. During the first twelve days of germination, while the seed protein decreases by about 34 gms., the free amino acids increase by some 14 gms. and asparagine by about 12 gms. Much of the nitrogen of the degraded protein can, therefore, be accounted for as free amino acids. A further large fraction can be accounted for in the form of the amide, asparagine. The remaining small fraction of protein nitrogen presumably has been transformed into glutamine and other nitrogenous compounds. In those plants, unlike lupine, which do not accumulate large quantities of asparagine, the amount of free amino acid formed is greatly increased, and is roughly equivalent to the amount of protein broken down. Unfortunately, completely satisfactory balance studies of protein broken down and soluble compounds formed are not available, although present-day techniques would permit such studies to be made. It seems, however, that the following transformations occur during seed germination:

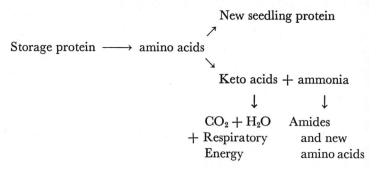

Thus, there is probably a competition for amino acids between the machinery for protein synthesis and the machinery for amino acid breakdown. If this is the case, then supplying either external nitrogen or respiratory substrates might, by mass action, slow the process of protein breakdown. Evidence in agreement with this thesis has been found. Paech (1935), for example, found that supplying either ammonium nitrate,

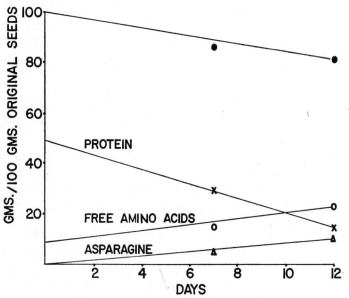

Figure 33. Changes in protein, free amino acids, and asparagine in Lupinus seeds after germination for 12 days in the dark. Adapted from Chibnall (1939).

TABLE XVII

Effects of $NH_4NO_3$, Urea, and Glucose on the
Degradation of Reserve Proteins[1]

| Nutrient | Endosperm or cotyledon | | Embryo | |
|---|---|---|---|---|
| | Protein N | Soluble N | Protein N | Soluble N |
| Triticum sativum[+] | (mg.) | (mg.) | (mg.) | (mg.) |
| Water | 35.7 | 12.4 | 23.4 | 14.8 |
| 0.5% $NH_4NO_3$ | 47.3 | 16.7 | 25.8 | 27.4 |
| Water | 34.0 | 13.4 | 22.0 | 12.3 |
| 0.5% Urea | 45.7 | 31.7 | 23.9 | 41.7 |
| Lupinus albus[++] | | | | |
| Nitrogen-free | 19.8 | 23.7 | 12.8 | 81.5 |
| Nitrogen-free plus 3% glucose | 46.8 | 36.0 | 12.0 | 49.7 |

[+] 5 days after germination.

[++] 14 days after germination.

[1] Adapted from Paech (1935).

urea, or glucose to young seedlings inhibits the breakdown of reserve seed protein (Table XVII). It would be of interest to determine whether a mixture of free amino acids is even more efficient at preventing protein breakdown. Likewise, it might be expected that specific inhibition of protein synthesis, or possibly amide synthesis, would inhibit the degradation of seed proteins.

Considering its importance to our knowledge of nitrogen metabolism, it is surprising that essentially nothing is known about the manner in which protein degradation occurs in seeds. It has always been assumed that proteolytic enzymes in the seeds are responsible for protein degradation and that free amino acids are the products of this breakdown. Although this seems likely, the facts that proteolytic enzymes occur in seeds (Balls and Hale, 1938) and that their proteolytic activity sometimes increases during germination (Bach, et al., 1927) do not constitute unequivocal evidence that proteolytic enzymes participate in protein degradation. For example, protein degradation might proceed, in part, by a reversal of protein synthesis, with the consequent formation of "activated" amino acids. The activated forms of amino acids currently known (amino acid-nucleotide compounds) are relatively unstable and would be degraded to free amino acids during any conventional isolation procedure. The formation of such activated amino acids has been postulated to explain the observation of Walter, *et al.* (1956) that the amino acids of preformed proteins are better precursors of new and different protein than free amino acids in the growing chick embryo. The resolution of the important problem of the nature of protein degradation should be the subject of considerable future investigation.

The question of whether protein synthesis occurs in the cotyledon during the massive degradation of proteins has been investigated only recently. Young (1957) has observed that the activity of an adenosine triphosphatase of pea cotyledons increases ten to fifteen-fold during the first five days of germination at 23°C. This increase is inhibited by dinitrophenol, p-fluorophenylalanine, and Chloramphenicol, all inhibitors of protein synthesis (Figure 34). Interestingly, this increase in enzyme activity depends upon the presence of either the growing shoot or root. If both are excised from the cotyledon, no activity develops. Likewise, no activity develops if the temperature is lowered from 23°C to 16°C. Similar results have been obtained concerning the appearance of amylase activity. In contrast to these activities, which may involve actual protein synthesis, proteolytic activity in the cotyledons increases only slightly on germination, and the increase is not affected by dinitrophenol, p-fluorophenylalanine, or Chloramphenicol.

*Breakdown of seed nucleic acid.* Unfortunately, little is known about this potentially important process during seed germination. However, evidence continues to increase indicating nucleic acid synthesis to be related to protein synthesis (Chapter 4). One would expect, therefore, that the developing seedling would require a supply of nucleic acid precursors, probably nucleotides. Such nucleotides could be supplied by *de novo* synthesis during germination (from amino acids, formate, carbon dioxide, and ribose phosphate), or they could be formed by the breakdown of existing nucleic acid in the seed. Oota, *et al.* (1953, 1954) have examined nucleic acid me-

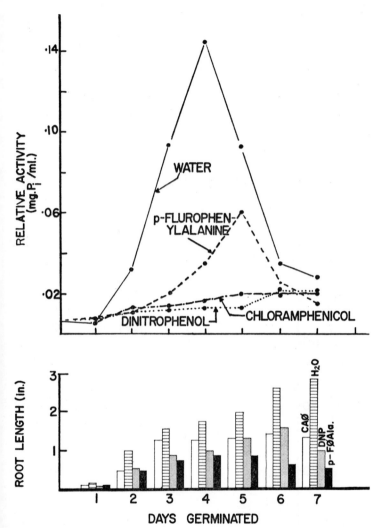

Figure 34. Effect of dinitrophenol, p-fluorophenylalanine, and Chloramphenicol on the development of adenosine triphosphatase activity in the cotyledons of germinating pea seeds. Adapted from Young (1957).

tabolism in germinating seeds, and have found surprisingly large quantities of ribonucleic acid stored in the cotyledons of *Vigna sesquipedalis.* Germination results in a steady decrease in the ribonucleic acid content of the seed. Figure 35 illustrates these changes in different portions of the seedling. Interestingly, the presence of the embryo is essential for breakdown of ribonucleic acid in the cotyledon. If embryos are detached from the cotyledons, no breakdown occurs (Oota, *et al.,* 1954). This could be due either to the embryo supplying some factor necessary for the breakdown of cotyledon ribonucleic acid, or to the inhibition of breakdown by mass action when the products of breakdown are not removed.

There are two known ways in which ribonucleic breakdown could occur in the cotyledons: (a) by the action of a ribonuclease-like diesterase with the resultant production of either

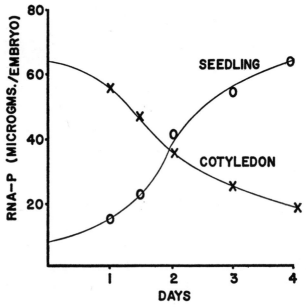

Figure 35. Changes in the ribonucleic acid content of cotyledons and the developing seedling during the germination of *Vigna sesquipedalis* (Oota, 1954).

nucleoside-3′ or nucleoside-5′-monophosphates, or (b) by the action of polynucleotide phosphorylase (Chapter 4) resulting in the formation of nucleoside-5′-diphosphates. The second possibility is better energetically, as a "high-energy" phosphate is produced which can engage directly in ribonucleic acid synthesis. However, the mode of breakdown is not yet known, and it will be interesting to find out exactly how storage ribonucleic acid is degraded during germination.

*Amino acid formation.* In addition to the breakdown of protein and nucleic acid, seed germination also initiates the synthesis of certain amino acids. For example, homoserine does not occur in pea seeds either in the free state or in protein (Virtanen, *et al.*, 1953). Within the twenty-four hours following the beginning of germination, however, homoserine can be detected by paper chromatography. The quantity of homoserine in seeds increases so rapidly that seventy-two hours after the beginning of germination, homoserine is present in greater quantity than any other amino acid (Virtanen, *et al.*, 1953). A vigorous synthesis of homoserine, therefore, occurs in response to germination. We know from studies with yeast (Chapter 2) that homoserine can be formed from aspartate via aspartyl phosphate. Whether this pathway is followed by germinating seeds (as seems likely), and whether the enzymes for homoserine synthesis are merely activated by germination or are synthesized *de novo* must be determined. As homoserine can act as a precursor for a number of amino acids, it is probable that the increased amount of homoserine produced by germination results in an increased supply of these amino acids for protein synthesis by the growing seedling.

The changes in levels of various free amino acids during germination have been examined to some extent. Virtanen, *et al.* (1953) found that ungerminated pea seeds contain a large amount of free glutamate and considerably smaller quantities of many other amino acids. As might be expected, germination results in a considerable increase in the quantities of all amino acids. However, the amounts of glutamate, serine, alanine, and arginine soon begin a steady decline. This temporary increase in certain amino acids, followed by a steady decrease, has also been noted by Kojima, *et al.* (1953) in germinating wheat, rice, and radish seeds. It is difficult to interpret these observations in the absence of data on the relative contributions of storage protein and *de novo* amino acid synthesis to the free amino acid pool, as well as the rates of amino acid utilization for protein synthesis and for energy production. It seems likely, however, that the changes in levels of various amino acids are chiefly a reflection of differences in their rates of production and utilization as germination progresses. By the employment of labeled compounds, it might be possible to determine the extent to which breakdown of storage protein and *de novo* synthesis contribute to the amount of each free amino acid formed, and also the extent that amino acid degradation competes with new protein synthesis for the utilization of each amino acid.

*Amide synthesis.* A fourth striking feature of the germination of many seeds is the formation of the amides, glutamine and asparagine, often in large quantities. Germinating lupine seedlings, for example, accumulate as much as 25% of their total nitrogen in the form of asparagine. This striking accumulation occurs only in the dark, as lupine germinated in the light accumulates only small amounts of asparagine. Furthermore, if dark-grown seedlings are placed in the light, the accumulated asparagine disappears. It was suggested many years ago that the accumulation of asparagine in etiolated seedlings is a response to starvation conditions under which the amino acids liberated by the degradation of storage protein are broken down to $CO_2$ and $H_2O$ as respiratory substrates (Borodin, 1878; Schulze, 1898; Chibnall, 1939). This produces increasing amounts of ammonia in each cell and Prianischnikov (1910, 1922) suggested that asparagine formation in the plant occurs chiefly as a mechanism for reducing this level of ammonia below toxic quantities. An alternative to this hypothesis has been that asparagine is accumulated by the liberation of asparagine from storage protein. Schulze (1898), however, found that the amount of asparagine accumulated by lupine greatly exceeds the amount already contained in stor-

TABLE XVIII

Production of Asparagine by Seedlings Supplied with Ammonium Chloride[1]

| Activity | increases in mg./100 seedlings over similar seedlings in N-free sol. | |
| --- | --- | --- |
| | Barley seedlings | Pea seedlings |
| Increase in total nitrogen | 15.7 | 196. |
| Increase in ammonia nitrogen | 0.3 | — |
| Increase in asparagine nitrogen | 19.6 | 182. |

[1] Plants germinated in water or in 0.1% $NH_4Cl$ for 14 days. (Prianischnikov' 1922).

age protein, so this hypothesis cannot be accepted. Furthermore, asparagine can be formed directly from ammonia taken up by a seedling from an external nutrient solution (Prianischnikov, 1922). Table XVIII shows that the ammonia taken up by a seedling accumulates as asparagine, not as free ammonia. However, the seedling must have a supply of available carbohydrate for asparagine synthesis to occur. If the seedlings are depleted of carbohydrate, then absorbed ammonia accumulates in the seedlings as ammonia. When glucose is given to the carbohydrate-depleted seedlings, however, ammonia decreases and asparagine increases (Prianischnikov and Schulow, 1910; Prianischnikov, 1922). Asparagine synthesis, therefore, can be induced in lupine seedlings when both ammonia and some carbon compound are present. This is exactly the situation that occurs during germination.

In many species asparagine is formed either during germination or in response to feeding the plants ammonia. In other plants glutamine is formed instead of asparagine, while in still others both glutamine and asparagine are formed. In all cases, however, the presence of increasing quantities of ammonia elicits amide formation. It seems likely that glutamine and asparagine are formed from glutamate and aspartate respectively by the enzymatic reactions already discussed (Chapter 3). All of the observations discussed above plus evidence obtained with radioactive isotopes are compatible with these mechanisms being operative in cellular amide synthesis.

It would appear, therefore, that amide accumulation is not

a unique feature of germination, but is related to protein hydrolysis simply by amide synthesis providing a means for the storage (in nontoxic form) of ammonia produced by deamination of the amino acids released during protein breakdown.

### GENERAL ASPECTS OF NITROGEN METABOLISM

Studies on protein synthesis by microorganisms, by animals, and especially by cell-free preparations of various living tissues (including plants) have demonstrated a number of requirements for protein synthesis. These include: a supply of free amino acids, a source of energy in the form of ATP, certain metal ions, a supply of nucleic acid precursors, and intact nucleic acid or nucleoprotein molecules. One would expect that these requirements might be apparent in intact plants in spite of the myriad of interfering reactions present in a highly organized group of cells. For example, it has been observed (Phillis and Mason, 1943) that protein levels in many plant tissues can be correlated with the levels of soluble nitrogen compounds (principally amino acids) in the plant cells. Although such findings have often been explained on the basis of a mass-action prevention of protein breakdown by free amino acids, it is just as reasonable to conclude that high cellular amino acid levels provide a non-limiting amino acid supply for protein synthesis. Thus, if the steady-state rate of synthesis increases in relation to the steady-state rate of breakdown, protein level will increase.

The necessity of an energy supply for maintenance of protein level is suggested by the often-observed (Chibnall, 1924; Mason and Maskell, 1928; Mothes, 1929) diurnal variation in protein level in leaves, in which the level decreases at night and rises during the day. However, if the leaves are exposed to continuous darkness, the protein level drops steadily with no daily cycling. The response of protein level, therefore, appears to be to light energy. Because an important product of the capture of light energy by leaves is ATP (Arnon, *et al.*, 1954), the physiological observations again may be explained by a known chemical process.

*Effects of ions on protein metabolism.* Two of the cations

presently implicated in the formation of peptide bonds, magnesium and potassium, likewise exert strong effects on the protein levels of intact plants. Potassium deficiency results in markedly decreased protein levels and concomitantly increased levels of free amino acids and amides (Richards and Templeman, 1936; Gregory and Sen, 1937). Potassium also promotes protein synthesis in potato tuber disks (Steward and Preston, 1941). Similarly, magnesium deficiency results in a decrease in protein and an increase in free amino acids and amides (Burrell, 1926; Steinberg, *et al.*, 1950). Although these ions are essential for many different phosphate transfer reactions, it seems possible that at least part of their effect is on protein synthesis directly.

Many other ions exert marked effects on the protein levels of plants, but in the absence of additional knowledge of their mode of action, it is useless to speculate on how they affect protein levels. Their effects, however, could easily be on some reaction many steps away from protein synthesis itself. Thus, deficiencies of phosphate, iron, sulfur, boron, and manganese all have been reported to produce lowered protein and increased amino acid levels in various plants. Copper deficiency, in contrast, may result in greater protein and total nitrogen levels (Gilbert, *et al.*, 1946; Gilbert, 1951).

*Effects of nucleic acid precursors and intact nucleic acids.* The steadily increasing mass of evidence that nucleic acids and nucleic acid synthesis are involved in protein synthesis has not been supplemented greatly by studies with intact higher plants. The studies which have been made, however, are quite striking. The apparent need for ribonucleic acid for protein synthesis in intact roots has been demonstrated by Brachet (1954, 1955), who has shown protein synthesis to be strongly inhibited by soaking the roots in ribonuclease. Interestingly, the roots can recover partially from the effects of ribonuclease upon the addition of yeast ribonucleic acid (Brachet, 1955).

Kessler (1956) has made important observations on the effects of uracil and thiouracil on protein levels in plants. Table XIX presents a portion of the observations, and shows

TABLE XIX

Effects of Uracil, Thiouracil, and Methyltryptophan on Protein and
Ribonucleic Acid Synthesis in Intact Plants[1]

| Addition to plant | Olive trees | | Grape vines | |
|---|---|---|---|---|
| | Protein N | RNA | Protein N | RNA |
| None | 1.61 | 0.81 | 1.71 | 0.60 |
| Uracil | 2.38 | 1.68 | 2.17 | 1.05 |
| Uracil plus thiouracil | 1.84 | 0.67 | 1.53 | 0.58 |
| Uracil plus methyltryptophan | 1.74 | 1.65 | 1.64 | 0.98 |

[1] Adapted from the data of Kessler (1956).

that uracil, when sprayed on olive trees or grape vines,
greatly increases the protein levels of the plant. This increase
is prevented if thiouracil, a uracil analogue, is present. The
results suggest that the supply of ribonucleic acid precursors
may be a limiting factor in protein synthesis in these plants.
This possibility is supported by Kessler's observation that
ribonucleic acid levels of both plants are greatly increased by
uracil, and that the increase is prevented by concomitant
addition of thiouracil. In addition to the effect of thiouracil,
the uracil-induced increase in protein levels is prevented by
the amino acid analogue, methyl tryptophan.

As far as they have been extended, all of the findings with
mature plants cited above are in accord with the picture of
protein synthesis being a process requiring energy, a supply
of amino acids, certain metal ions (probably magnesium and
either potassium or sodium), nucleic acid, and possibly the
synthesis of nucleic acid. It should be noted that the many
results obtained with intact plants are far more understand-
able when viewed in the light of our knowledge of the biochemistry of protein synthesis (Chapter 4) than when they are
viewed alone.

*Effect of excision on the nitrogen metabolism of an organ.*
An important question in the study of nitrogen metabolism
of intact plants concerns whether each organ constituting
the whole plant is capable of performing independently the
reactions involved in the conversion of simple nitrogen com-

pounds into protein and other macromolecules, or whether some organs depend upon others for all or a part of the necessary metabolic transformations. Although useful information is only available on certain organs, the findings are of considerable interest. Roots apparently possess all of the enzymes required to transform simple substances into protein. When roots are excised from a plant, they can readily be grown in tissue culture in the presence of simple nutrients and vitamins, and are thus essentially independent of the remainder of the plant. In contrast, when leaves are excised, the protein content of the leaves decreases markedly, with equivalent increase in non-protein nitrogen (Schulze and Bosshard, 1885; Chibnall, 1924). The protein decrease is not due to starvation, as the decrease occurs in the light when ample photosynthesis is occurring. As might be expected from our knowledge of protein breakdown in germinating seeds, much of the nitrogen liberated by protein degradation in leaves accumulates in the leaf cells in the form of glutamine and asparagine. This amide accumulation must be due to a secondary synthesis of glutamine and asparagine, as only small amounts of these amides occur in leaf protein. Yemm (1937), in a study of the metabolism of detached barley leaves in the dark, found that amides accumulate during the first forty-eight to ninety-six hours following excision. Thereafter, the levels of amino acids and amides decline steadily and free ammonium ions accumulate in large quantities. Likewise, the respiration of the leaves, which originally is at the expense of carbohydrate, gradually involves other materials, presumably including keto acids derived from amino acids. Similar studies by Vickery, *et al.* (1937) on detached tobacco leaves in the light showed comparable results as to great protein decrease and great soluble nitrogen increase. Further evidence that the protein decrease is not related to starvation comes from their finding that the tobacco leaves increased in carbohydrate and in dry weight, due to photosynthesis, while the striking protein decrease occurred. Interestingly, tobacco leaves in the light accumulated glutamine, while leaves in the dark accumulated asparagine. Free ammonia only accumulated during the later stages of protein decrease in the dark.

Wood, *et al.* (1943, 1944; Cruickshank and Wood, 1945), in a comprehensive study of protein degradation in detached leaves, observed that protein breakdown by detached leaves of Kikuyu grass is strongly inhibited by the absence of oxygen, and that amino acids, but no amides, accumulate. It is easy to see why amides fail to accumulate, as their synthesis requires the ATP produced by respiration. The inhibition of protein breakdown is very puzzling, however. As protein breakdown is not a result of respiratory starvation, the question again arises as to whether energy is needed for protein breakdown as it is for amide synthesis. It would be of considerable interest to learn whether dinitrophenol, which would stop energy production without stopping respiration, would also inhibit protein breakdown.

There is little doubt, from the above results, that detached leaves differ from attached leaves in some way which results in an extensive breakdown of their protein. Despite the many investigations on this problem, the reason why the degradation occurs is completely obscure. It could be due to any of several factors. One might suppose, for example, that the leaf cannot make certain amino acids or other precursors which are supplied by the plant. This could result in a steady breakdown. The finding of Chibnall (1954) that the induction of roots on the petioles of detached leaves inhibits leaf protein breakdown is consistent with the thesis that leaves are supplied some factor by the roots which maintains normal protein levels. The possibility that leaves cannot make all of their amino acids has been examined both by Rogers (1955) and by Racusen and Aronoff (1954). Rogers has reported that leaves can incorporate the carbons of either $C^{14}$-sucrose or $C^{14}$-acetate into all amino acids, while Racusen and Aronoff have found that young leaves, at least, can incorporate $C^{14}O_2$ into most, if not all, amino acids. In some cases, however, the rates of incorporation are quite slow, so it is possible that leaves are unable to produce sufficient amounts of one or more amino acids to support normal steady-state rates of protein synthesis. Alternatively, leaves may not be able to produce some other factor (nucleic acid precursors, for example) necessary for protein synthesis, or some factor which inhibits breakdown. It would be of considerable interest to learn whether externally supplied amino acids or nucleotides inhibit protein degradation in detached leaves. In line with this, Bonner and Haagen-Smit (1939) reported that growth of excised leaf disks is enhanced by the presence of adenine in the sucrose nutrient medium. Of greatest interest, however, is the finding of Richmond and Lang (1957) that kinetin (6-furfurylaminopurine) reduces protein breakdown of detached leaves in a striking manner. Figure 36 illustrates that 5 mg. per liter of kinetin reduces the protein loss of detached *Xanthium* leaves to 15% instead of the 60% loss in untreated leaves. The mechanism of kinetin action is not clear, but the pre-

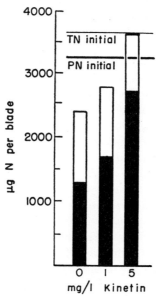

Figure 36. Effects of kinetin on the protein nitrogen (PN) and total nitrogen (TN) of detached *Xanthium* leaves after 12 days. Solid bars represent protein nitrogen, total bars represent total nitrogen, horizontal lines represent initial values (Richmond and Lang, 1957).

liminary observation that kinetin (1 mg. per liter) does not affect the incorporation of amino acids into the protein of cell-free extracts of pea seedlings (Webster, 1957) suggests that kinetin may not affect protein synthesis directly. Perhaps it acts directly on the mechanism of protein degradation, or on nucleic acid metabolism. In any event, the significant observation of Richmond and Lang (1957) raises a question as to whether kinetin or some closely related substance might not be a factor (or one of the factors) supplied by the plant to the leaves to maintain normal protein levels. Certainly, the capacity for protein synthesis has not been lost when leaves are detached from the plant, as both Racusen and Aronoff (1954) and Chibnall and Wiltshire (1954) have presented evidence that protein synthesis is still proceeding during the overwhelming protein degradation in excised leaves. It would appear that the solution of this problem will demand knowledge of (a) whether detachment decreases the absolute rate of protein synthesis or increases the rate of degradation; (b) the nature of the degradation process; (c) how the degradation is influenced by added amino acids, nucleotides, and other substances (such as kinetin) which may be translocated into the leaves from the roots.

*Translocation of nitrogenous compounds.* One of the most important problems relative to the overall nitrogen metabolism in a higher plant concerns the movement of nitrogenous substances between organs, and the importance of such movement to the metabolism of each organ. The above paragraphs, describing the importance of roots to the metabolism of leaves, serve to emphasize this problem. Although one might expect nitrogen to be translocated in an inorganic form from the roots to the various other organs of the plant, this does not seem always to be the case. Bollard (1953) examined the tracheal sap of apple trees and found practically no inorganic nitrogen being translocated. Instead, about 90% of the translocated nitrogen was in the form of glutamate, glutamine, aspartate, and asparagine. The remaining 10% consisted chiefly of alanine, γ-aminobutyrate, arginine, leucine, methionine, serine, threonine, tyrosine, and valine, plus some unidentified peptides. Wolffgang and Mothes (1953) similarly found that nitrogen is transported chiefly as asparagine in the elm, although detectable quantities of aspartate, glutamate, proline, and a glutamate-containing peptide were present. In the *Betulaceae*, citrulline accounts for all or almost all of the transported nitrogen (Wolffgang and Mothes, 1953; Reuter and Wolffgang, 1954). Most surprising has been the observation that allantoin and allantoic acid constitute as much as 100% of the transported nitrogen of various *Acer* species, and major portions of such nitrogen in the *Borraginaceae*, *Platanaceae*, *Hypocastanaceae*, and *Papilionaceae* (Mothes and Engelbrecht, 1952, 1954; Engelbrecht, 1954). In *Nicotiana*, *Datura*, and *Atropa*, alkaloids constitute a portion of the nitrogen transported out of the root (Mothes, 1955). Schmid (1948) reported that nicotine represents the major nitrogenous compound in tobacco sap, and Mothes (1955) has suggested that it may be the principal form (together with some amino acids) in which assimilated nitrogen is translocated from tobacco roots.

The above results have been extended considerably by Bollard (1956), who examined the composition of the tracheal sap of a large number of different plants. Nitrate was present in less than half of the saps tested, and was always in trace amounts. In most species examined, nitrogen was translocated principally in the form of glutamine or asparagine, with smaller quantities of glutamate, aspartate, alanine, serine, threonine, methionine, and valine usually present. In twenty-nine different species citrulline was translocated in varying quantities, while allantoin or allantoic acid were present in the saps of twenty-three different species. In all of the above cases, the material examined is being translocated upward in the xylem from the roots. Only limited studies have been performed on phloem transport, but they indicate relatively low concentrations of ninhydrin-positive material moving through the phloem (Kennedy and Mittler, 1953). This nitrogenous material is composed of glutamate, glutamine, aspartate, and asparagine. Additional amino acids, as well as increased amounts of glutamate, aspartate and their amides, are found in phloem during the rapid growth of leaves or during their senescence.

## NITROGEN METABOLISM DURING AGING

The question of what happens to metabolism as a cell ages, as well as why it ages at all, is important whether one is interested in either animals or plants. Surprisingly little is known concerning the chemical nature of the aging process in cells, or of the metabolic changes which accompany it. The present discussion, therefore, will be concerned with some of the engrossing problems that need clarification, rather than with attempting to construct a picture of metabolic aging from our present limited information.

In contrast to germinating and rapidly growing seedlings, where all emphasis is on active synthesis of protein and nucleic acid, the mature plant exhibits either a stable protein level or a tendency towards protein loss. With the exception of the striking synthesis of protein in ripening seeds, most mature plant parts show little overall change in protein level under normal conditions (Gregory, 1937). This does not mean, however, that their protein is metabolically inactive. All evidence with both stable and radioactive isotopes indicates that the proteins of mature plant organs undergo continuous breakdown and resynthesis (Vickery, et al., 1940; Hevesy, et al., 1940; MacVicar and Burris, 1948; Webster, 1954; Stephenson, et al., 1956; Webster, et al., 1957). If this is the case, then the increasing protein levels of young cells, the stable protein levels of mature cells, and the decreasing protein levels of senescent cells are chiefly reflections of varying ratios of the steady-state synthesis and breakdown of cellular protein. What factors affect the ratio of synthesis to breakdown? Apparently, there are many. As might be expected, protein levels are strongly influenced by the amount of nitrogen supplied to the plant. Nitrogen deficiency, however, has a differential effect on the protein levels of cells of different ages (Gregory and Sen, 1937). Figure 37 illustrates these differences, and shows that differences in protein levels of normal leaves appear only in relatively old leaves (line A). However, if less

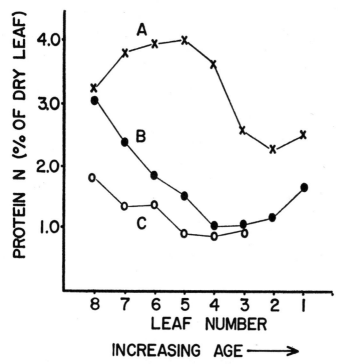

Figure 37. Differential protein loss in barley leaves of different ages, grown under decreasing concentrations of nitrogen. A., normal nitrogen supply; B., 1/9 normal nitrogen supply; C., 1/81 normal nitrogen supply (adapted from Gregory and Sen, 1937).

nitrogen is supplied to the plant (line B), then the more mature leaves (leaves 4–7) lose protein in amounts roughly in line with their ages. Even the very old leaves (leaves 1–3), whose protein levels are already lowered, effect a further decrease in protein. Only in extreme states of nitrogen deficiency (line C) are the protein levels of very young leaves (leaf 8) reduced considerably.

Although one might suspect that this tendency of old leaves to lose protein readily is due to a loss in their ability to synthesize new protein, this does not appear to be the case. When plants are grown under conditions of severe nitrogen de-

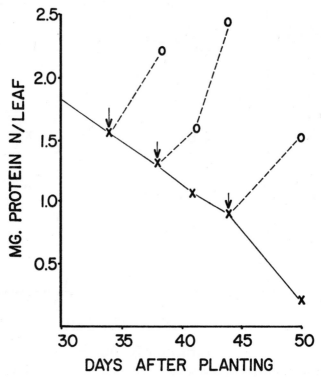

Figure 38. Recovery of protein by leaves of different ages after elimination of nitrogen deficiency. Solid lines, protein level under nitrogen deficiency; dotted line, protein level after addition of nitrogen as indicated by arrows (Walkley, 1940).

ficiency, the protein level of any single leaf declines steadily. Figure 38 shows, however, that if ample nitrogen is supplied to the plant, the leaf is perfectly capable of recovering its normal protein level (Walkley, 1940). These observations, plus the findings with isotopes, suggest that the decrease in protein level in aging cells is not due to an impairment of the actual machinery for protein synthesis. This does not mean, of course, that the decrease in protein level is not due to a slowing of the rate of protein synthesis, but does mean that the potential for protein synthesis appears to be just as great in a mature cell as in a young cell.

If the decrease in protein level of aging cells is not due to a degradation of the protein synthesis machinery, then there are a number of alternative possibilities which should be examined. Some of these are:

a. Aging might increase the effectiveness of the machinery for protein degradation.
b. Aging might reduce the ability of a cell to produce certain precursors at the rates found in young cells.
c. Aging might reduce the effectiveness of some auxiliary process (such as ATP production) necessary for protein synthesis.
d. Aging might prevent the entry of essential substances into an organ through a selective block of translocation.
e. Aging might result in the accumulation of a natural inhibitor of some process necessary for protein synthesis.

Some of the most interesting findings on the effects of aging on nitrogen metabolism have come from studies on fruit ripening. Here, the cells often age in a spectacular and easily recognizable manner. The metabolic changes associated with aging in ripening fruit have been studied very little, but the idea has arisen that such aging is associated with degenerative processes. Experimental evidence at hand is not compatible with this thesis. For example, Marks, *et al.* (1957) have shown that the changes associated with fruit ripening in tomatoes (synthesis of lycopenes, etc.) are dependent upon a continual supply of energy. If oxidative phosphorylation is stopped with dinitrophenol, the fruit remains green and continues to exhibit the properties of an unripe fruit. Hulme (1948, 1954) has observed that the total protein of apple fruit increases steadily during ripening. Similarly, Tager (1956) has shown that several enzymes are synthesized in connection with the ripening of bananas. It would seem, therefore, that aging in fruits is a process dependent upon the synthesis of proteins and other substances, and may be prevented by preventing such syntheses. This is an important concept and certainly deserves further examination. It will be of great interest to learn whether aging in all kinds of cells is dependent upon a continual energy supply for the synthesis of substances associated with the aging process. Likewise, it is important to learn how these syntheses are related to the senescence and death of a cell, and whether such processes can be inhibited or reversed. Although the process of cellular aging has not been investigated intensively, it would appear to be one of the more challenging and fruitful problems for both biochemists and physiologists.

## REFERENCES

ARNON, D. E., ALLEN, M. B., AND WHATLEY, F. R., Nature 174, 394 (1954).

BACH, A., OPARIN, A., AND WAHNER, R., Biochem. Zeit. 180, 363 (1927).

BALLS, A. K. AND HALE, W. S., Cereal Chem. 15, 622 (1938).

BOLLARD, E. G., Nature 171, 571 (1953).

BOLLARD, E. G., Nature 178, 1189 (1956).

BONNER, D. AND HAAGEN-SMIT, A. J., Proc. Natl. Acad. Sci. 25, 184 (1939).

BORODIN, I., Botan. Zeitung 36, 802 (1878).

BRACHET, J., Nature 174, 876 (1954).

BRACHET, J., Biochim. Biophys. Acta 16, 611 (1955).

BURRELL, R. C., Botan. Gazette 82, 320 (1926).

CHIBNALL, A. C., Biochem. Jour. 18, 395 (1924).

CHIBNALL, A. C., Protein Metabolism in the Plant, Yale University Press, New Haven (1939).

CHIBNALL, A. C., New Phytologist 53, 31 (1954).

CHIBNALL, A. C. AND WILTSHIRE, G. H., New Phytologist 53, 38 (1954).

CRUICKSHANK, D. H. AND WOOD, J. G., Australian Jour. Exp. Biol. Med. Sci. 23, 243 (1945).

ENGELBRECHT, L., Flora 142, 25, 501 (1954).

GILBERT, S. G., Plant Physiol. 26, 398 (1951).

GILBERT, S. G., SELL, H. M., AND DROSDOFF, M., Plant Physiol. 21, 290 (1946).

GREGORY, F. G., Ann. Rev. Biochem. 6, 557 (1937).

GREGORY, F. G. AND SEN, P. K., Ann. Botany, N. S. 1, 521 (1937).

HEVESY, G., LINDERSTROM-LANG, K., KESTON, A. S., AND OLSEN, C., Compt. rend. trav. lab. Carlsberg Ser. Chim. 23, 213 (1940).

HULME, A. C., Biochem. Jour. 43, 343 (1948).

HULME, A. C., Jour. Exp. Botany 5, 159 (1954).

KENNEDY, J. S. AND MITTLER, T. E., Nature 171, 528 (1953).

KESSLER, B., Nature 178, 1337 (1956).

KOJIMA, H., YATAZAWA, M., AND GOTO, Y., Sci. Reports Shiga Ag. College, Ser. I., No. 451 (1953).

MACVICAR, R. AND BURRIS, R., Jour. Biol. Chem. 176, 511 (1948).

MARKS, J. D., BERNLOHR, R. W., AND VARNER, J. E., Plant Physiol 32, 259 (1957).

MASON, T. G. AND MASKELL, E. J., Ann. Botany 42, 189 (1928).

MOTHES, K., Planta 7, 585 (1929).

MOTHES, K., Ann. Rev. Plant Physiol. 6, 393 (1955).

MOTHES, K. AND ENGELBRECHT, L., Flora 139, 586 (1952).

MOTHES, K. AND ENGELBRECHT, L., Flora 141, 356 (1954).

OOTA, Y. AND OSAWA, S., Experientia 10, 254 (1954).

OOTA, Y., FUJII, R., AND OSAWA, S., Jour. Biochem. (Japan) 40, 649 (1953).

PAECH, K., Planta **24**, 78 (1935).

PHILLIS, E. AND MASON, T. G., Memoirs Cotton Res. Sta. Trinidad **B15**, 469 (1943).

PRIANISCHNIKOV, D., Ber. **40**, 242 (1922).

PRIANISCHNIKOV, D. AND SCHULOW, P., Ber. **28**, 253 (1910).

RACUSEN, D. AND ARONOFF, S., Arch. Biochem. Biophys. **51**, 68 (1954).

REUTER, G. AND WOLFFGANG, H., Flora **142**, 146 (1954).

RICHARDS, R. J. AND TEMPLEMAN, W. G., Ann. Botany **50**, 367 (1936).

RICHMOND, A. E. AND LANG, A., Science **125**, 651 (1957).

ROGERS, B. J., Plant Physiol. **30**, 377 (1955).

SCHMID, H., Ber. Schweiz. Botan. Ges. **58**, 5 (1948).

SCHULZE, E., Zeit. physiol. Chem. **24**, 18 (1898).

SCHULZE, E. AND BOSSHARD, E., Zeit. physiol. Chem. **9**, 420 (1885).

STEINBERG, R. A., BOWLING, J. D., AND MCMURTREY, J. E., JR., Plant Physiol. **25**, 279 (1950).

STEPHENSON, M. L., THIMANN, K. V., AND ZAMECNIK, P. C., Arch. Biochem. Biophys. **65**, 194 (1956).

STEWARD, F. C. AND PRESTON, C., Plant Physiol. **16**, 85 (1941).

TAGER, J. M., So. African Jour. Sci. **53**, 167 (1956).

VICKERY, H. B., PUCHER, G. W., WAKEMAN, A. J., AND LEAVENWORTH, C. S., Conn. Ag. Exp. Sta. Bulletin 399 (1937).

VICKERY, H. B., PUCHER, G. W., SCHOENHEIMER, R., AND RITTENBERG, D., Jour. Biol. Chem. **135**, 531 (1940).

VIRTANEN, A. I., BERG, A. M., AND KARI, S., Acta Chem. Scand. **7**, 1423 (1953).

WALKLEY, J., New Phytologist **39**, 362 (1940).

WALTER, H., BULBENKO, A., AND MAHLER, H. R., Nature **178**, 1176 (1956).

WEBSTER, G. C., Plant Physiol. **29**, 382 (1954).

WEBSTER, G. C., in *Chemical Basis of Heredity* (McElroy, W. D. and Glass, B., Eds.), Johns Hopkins Press, Baltimore (1957).

WEBSTER, G. C., BERNER, R. A., AND GANSA, A., Plant Physiol. **32**, 60 (1957).

WOLFFGANG, H. AND MOTHES, K., Naturwissenschaften **40**, 606 (1953).

WOOD, J. G., CRUICKSHANK, D. H., AND KUCHEL, R. H., Australian Jour. Exp. Biol. Med. Sci. **21**, 37 (1943), **22**, 111 (1944).

WOOD, J. G., MERCER, F. V., AND PEDLOW, C., Australian Jour. Exp. Biol. Med. Sci. **22**, 37 (1944).

YEMM, E. W., Proc. Roy. Soc. London, **B117**, 483, 504 (1935), 123, 243 (1937).

YOUNG, J. L., Federation Proc. **16**, 275 (1957).

# Index